THE COAST-TO-COAST WALK:

ROCKS AND SCENERY

Barry Butler & John Gunner

DISCLAIMER

The authors have taken all reasonable care to ensure that the information in this guide is accurate and up-to-date. However, they cannot accept responsibility for unforeseen circumstances that may arise during the Walk. Paths and rights of way may be changed, and the weather can affect the safety of some routes. Walkers are strongly advised to check the availability of local transport, accommodation, and any other facilities they may rely on. If you discover any significant changes that future walkers may need to be aware of, please let us know, in the first instance by contacting the Publishers.

2QT Limited (Publishing)

First edition 2017
2QT Limited (Publishing)
www.2qt.co.uk

Typesetting by Dale Rennard

Printed in Malta on behalf of Latitude Press Ltd.

A CIP catalogue record for this book is available
from the British Library

ISBN 978-1-912014-52-1

Contents

ACKNOWLEDGEMENTS

We are grateful to many people who contributed in so many ways to the completion of this guide:

Dr Joachim Schneibel and Alan Staniforth each walked the entire Walk with a draft of the book in hand; their comments on specific locations and on the general presentation were particularly valuable. Janet Arnison, John and Judith Dixon, Ted Ferguson, Mike and Sue Maxwell, and Angela White made valuable comments on parts of the Lake District section. Dr Pat Murphy reviewed a draft of the whole book. The early stages of the project benefited from discussions with Dr Andrew Bell. Professor Mike Branney gave helpful advice on the detailed interpretation of the boulder at Loc. **L33**. Professor Donald Fraser helped with the characterisation of a piece of the Ennerdale Granite. Members of our families – Joe Butler, Judith Gunner, Donna Kirkhope, Susannah Wilson – have helped in a variety of ways. Mike and Bénédicte Windle provided invaluable support and discussions throughout the project.

We thank Catherine Cousins and the team at 2QT for their care and skills in bringing the book to publication.

Barry Butler is especially grateful to his wife, Louise, for her wonderful companionship and wise counsel. Sadly she did not live to see the completion of the Coast-to-Coast project. For his part, this book is a tribute to her.

THE COUNTRYSIDE CODE

As you walk, keep in mind that farmers and others depend on the countryside, including open moorland and mountains, for their livelihood. All forms of wildlife – animals, birds, flowers, and trees – are totally dependent on the natural environment and its preservation.

A simple rule is to leave no evidence of your passing. Make sure that livestock is safe, gates left as you found them, and wildlife undisturbed. If you are looking at rocks, remove any sharp fragments that could harm animals. Take all your litter away with you.

PERSONAL SAFETY

Plan each day's walk. Take maps and a compass. Wear clothing suitable for the range of altitudes and weather conditions. Take enough food and liquid.

The best rock exposures are often near cliffs, but don't go near cliff edges or overhangs. Smooth rocks, whether on the coast or inland, are often slippery.

GRID REFERENCES

Grid references provide the most precise method of locating a point on the ground – to within 100 metres or, for even greater precision, to within 10 metres. They can be used in conjunction with the Global Positional System. We use as an example Ivelet Bridge in the centre of Swaledale:

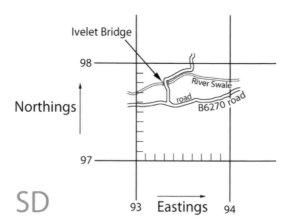

To determine its Grid Reference :

1. Look in a corner of the map sheet for the two-letter name of the 100-kilometre square. For Ivelet Bridge this is SD.

2. Determine the "Easting" of the location. Find the two-digit number of the N-S grid line on the left of the location – this is 93; then measure or estimate the third figure – this is 3. So the Easting of the grid reference is 933.

3. Similarly, using the E-W grid lines, determine the "Northing" of the location. This is 978.

So the complete 6-figure Grid Reference is SD 933 978.

INTRODUCTION

WHY WE WROTE THIS BOOK AND WHO IT IS FOR

If you want to know more about rocks and scenery you could hardly do better than to take a walk through some of England's finest and most varied countryside and see it all for yourself. The route of the Coast–to–Coast Walk across northern England, devised by Alfred Wainwright in 1973, might have been chosen specially to show off the fascinating story of what our country is made of, and how it came to be so.

The book is designed to be a companion and guide for everyone interested in the natural environment. The Walk takes us through much of the history of northern England during the past 500 million years. The story includes such dramas as a continental collision uniting what is now Scotland and northern Ireland with England and Wales, and the slow drift of Britain from south of the Equator through different climatic zones to its present position in the northern hemisphere. The most recent part of the history was an Ice Age which created much of the magnificent scenery of the country and the surface we walk on today.

Over millions of years the Earth's crust has been moulded by powerful processes, constantly moving and evolving. The area of northern England has been at various times covered by deep sea, volcanoes, deserts, rivers, ice, and by great thicknesses of rock which has now been eroded away. Rocks and scenery are the pages of the book that tells this long turbulent history. Sometimes the pages are revealed on a grand scale; at other times we need to look at the smallest details to understand what the rocks are telling us. We shall do our best to translate Earth's history book into plain language and to share with you the excitement of our subject.

HOW THE BOOK IS ORGANISED

We have followed these principles in writing the book:

- We assume that your primary purpose is the achievement of walking the distance from St Bees to Robin Hood's Bay. So we keep the descriptions of what you see while walking as short as possible.

- Different parts of the text appear in different kinds of type as follows:

  - The rocks and scenery at specific Locations are described in sequence as they come into view along the line of the Walk. This part of the text is in black type.

  - *Brief descriptions of the Walk from one Location to the next are in italic type with a grey background.*

  - More detailed explanations of what you have seen, or what you will see, are provided in a "Journal", in blue type, which you can read at any time. It will be most effective if you can read it soon before or just after the day's walking.

- Geological ideas and methods are developed as the Walk progresses. You don't need any previous knowledge of rocks and scenery.

- We avoid using technical terms but where they have to be used they are highlighted in **bold** type and defined in the Glossary.

- We describe only what you can see from the Route, though we will sometimes refer to evidence from a wider area when it increases the interest and understanding of the explanation.

By the time you reach Robin Hood's Bay we think you will be pleasantly surprised at how much you understand about the way the Earth works and about the evolution of northern England.

The Walk divides naturally into stages, both in the type of walking and in the rocks and scenery of each region. We use these letters for identifying the Locations and Figures:

- **C** the west Coastal region, from St Bees to Cleator
- **L** the Lake District, from Cleator to Shap Abbey
- **R** Ravenstonedale, from Shap Abbey to Kirkby Stephen
- **D** the Yorkshire Dales, from Kirkby Stephen to Catterick Bridge
- **V** the Vale of Mowbray, from Catterick Bridge to Ingleby Arncliffe
- **M** the North York Moors, from Ingleby Arncliffe to Robin Hood's Bay.

To make it easy to match Figures to Locations we use the same number for each.

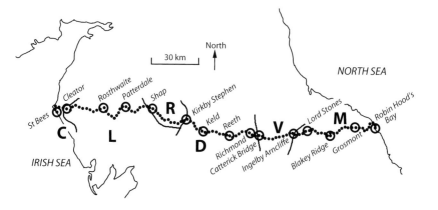

From Cleator to Robin Hood's Bay, the rocks get progressively younger; the chart on the next page shows the ages of the rocks we shall see on the Walk. Because rocks get younger upwards, you have to read the chart, and the direction of the Walk, from the bottom upwards.

A WORD ABOUT MAPS AND ROUTE–FINDING

The maps and the Route descriptions in this book are to help identify the Locations. They are not detailed enough for route–finding, especially in conditions of poor visibility. You will definitely need more–detailed maps. For safe walking we recommend Geographers' *A–Z Coast to Coast Walk* – the complete route in a compact booklet – or Harvey Maps' *Coast to Coast West* and *Coast to Coast East* sheets. Various apps provide high–quality digital maps, such as the UK Map by Phil Endecott. There are several descriptive guides to the Walk, including an updated edition of Alfred Wainwright's original guidebook.

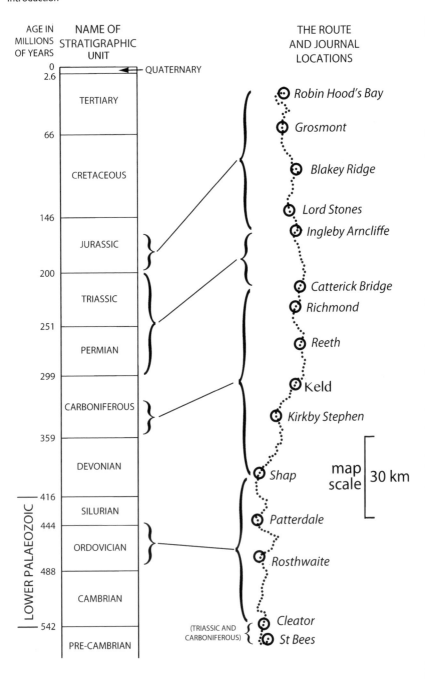

AGE IN MILLIONS OF YEARS	NAME OF STRATIGRAPHIC UNIT		THE ROUTE AND JOURNAL LOCATIONS
0		QUATERNARY	
2.6			
	TERTIARY		Robin Hood's Bay
			Grosmont
66			
	CRETACEOUS		Blakey Ridge
			Lord Stones
146			Ingleby Arncliffe
	JURASSIC		
200			Catterick Bridge
	TRIASSIC		Richmond
251			
	PERMIAN		Reeth
299			Keld
	CARBONIFEROUS		Kirkby Stephen
359			
	DEVONIAN		Shap
416			
	SILURIAN		Patterdale
444			
	ORDOVICIAN		Rosthwaite
488			
	CAMBRIAN		Cleator
542			St Bees
	PRE-CAMBRIAN	(TRIASSIC AND CARBONIFEROUS)	

LOWER PALAEOZOIC

map scale 30 km

JOURNAL I – ST BEES

We use the first stage of the Walk – from St Bees to Cleator, crossing rocks from Carboniferous to Triassic in age – to introduce ways of looking at rocks and scenery. And we start with a very short issue of the Journal to present some essential ideas.

BEDROCK AND SUPERFICIAL ROCKS

The coastal scenery at St Bees was formed in the last few thousand years, during and after the Ice Age. In complete contrast, the red rocks in the cliffs were made 240 million years ago in a desert region near the centre of a supercontinent a few degrees north of the Equator. How all this came about will become clear in the course of the Walk.

It's convenient to make a distinction between **bedrock** (meaning rocks formed before the Ice Age, which began about 2.6 million years ago) and **superficial rocks** (meaning the younger rocks that cover the bedrock). On the Walk we shall see both bedrock and superficial rocks and scenery.

Because the Ice Age was geologically so recent, ending only 10,000 years ago, the effects of the glaciers and ice sheets on rocks and scenery are evident everywhere. The generally smoothed topography of the St Bees headland, inland from the cliffs, is the result of a combination of both erosion and deposition during the glaciation.

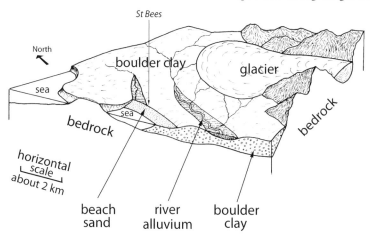

*An impression of a small part of the western Lake District towards the end of the Ice Age, based on the St Bees area. Ice originally covered all the lowland and extended over the sea. **Boulder clay**, river **alluvium**, and beach sand are all classed as superficial deposits covering the bedrock.*

BEDS AND BEDDING PLANES

The cliffs on the west side of St Bees Head are made of red **sandstones**. A characteristic of these and most other **sedimentary rocks** is that they were deposited as layers or **beds**.

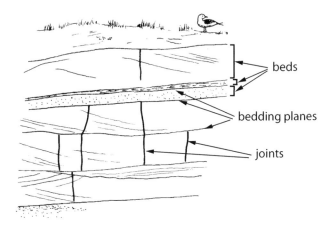

*A sequence of beds of sandstone in the cliffs at St Bees. The surfaces between the beds are called **bedding planes**. Structures inside the beds (like the fainter oblique lines) can be used to find out about the environment of the time. The nearly vertical **joints** are cracks formed after the beds had solidified into rock. Although they are often prominent features of an exposure, they usually provide little information about how the rocks were made.*

St Bees Priory Church, west door.
The local rock makes fine building stone.

1. THE WEST COASTAL REGION

The first part of the Walk is on rocks of Triassic age, magnificently exposed in the coastal cliffs but inland covered by superficial rocks. The Walk continues on Carboniferous rocks, completely covered by superficial rocks. We use this section of the Walk as a simple introduction to some ideas about how to look at rocks and scenery.

THE WALK – ST BEES TO CLEATOR

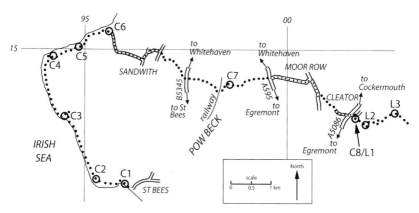

St Bees to Cleator

THE PRESENT AS A KEY TO THE PAST

Location **C1**, NX 960 118, at "Wainwright's Wall". As you zip, button, and strap yourself into your kit for the first day of your Walk, give some thought to the scene around you.

*Fig. **C1**. The foreshore at the north end of St Bees beach.*

Everything you can see is in motion, driven by the forces of the Sun, the wind, the waves, and the gravitational attraction of the Earth itself. Even the rocks are changing, though slowly by human standards. The cliff is being weathered and eroded by frost and rain, seabirds and sheep, and the people ten minutes ahead of you on the Walk. The pebbles and sand on the shore are constantly moved by waves, tides, and by the stream that enters the bay at the north end of the promenade. And imagine the activity beyond the ever–changing shoreline, with marine fauna and flora, and vast quantities of sand, mud, seashells, and terrestrial debris. This postcard view provides clues to much of what we shall see in the next 300 km, and the means to understand it by using the present day to model processes in the past.

From the north end of St Bees beach walk along the coast path for ¾ km to the next Location. On the way, near the top of the cliff, you pass the fenced–off Pattering Holes – open joints in the rocks below ground level.

DIFFERENCES WITHIN SANDSTONES

Loc. **C2**, NX 952 119, at the top of the cliff where there is a concrete shelter with explanatory signboards. Take a look at the rocks in the low vertical face a few metres north of the signboards.

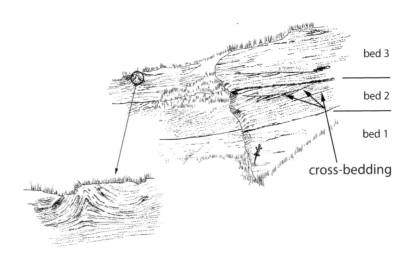

*Fig. C2. Three **beds** of **sandstone** (solidified sand) are labelled 1, 2, and 3 in the drawing. They are marked by slight differences in their red colours, and by differences in their internal structures.*

Bed 1 is almost the same throughout its vertical thickness and was probably deposited very quickly.

Bed 2 is made up of numerous smaller beds, and the **bedding planes** between them are slightly tilted. This is called **cross–bedding**, and results from a stream entering an area of still water and depositing its load of sand as tilted layers.

The feature shown in bed 3 (and in more detail in the inset) indicates that when it first formed the sediment was like a quicksand. Excess water at the time of deposition escaped, with distortion of the bedding (the structure is sometimes called a sand volcano).

The rocks at this Location were formed about 240 million years ago, in the Triassic period (see the chart in the Introduction). The processes that made them were broadly similar to those in the stream at the north end of Wainwright's Wall, with the difference that here the environment was a desert and the streams flowed only occasionally. Dinosaurs were just beginning to evolve; the Common Lizard near the bottom of the drawing is a relative of his more terrible reptilian ancestors.

Continue along the top of the cliff for 1¾ km to where the coast path comes down to sea level.

MORE SANDSTONES

Loc. **C3**, NX 945 134, Fleswick. These are the same kind of rocks as at the last Location, but there are more to see.

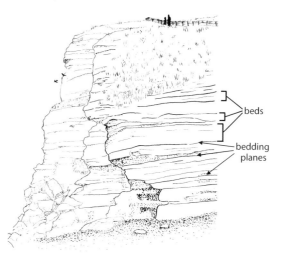

beds

bedding planes

Fig. C3. The north side of the inlet at Fleswick, from the shore. (You don't need to find the exact viewpoint, but if you want to, it is close to where the stream meets the beach).

The continuity of individual beds across the width of the exposure and still further along the cliffs implies that they extend laterally for a long distance. The general similarity of the beds over the full height of the cliff, notably the sandy nature and the red colour (an indication of a hot arid environment), implies a similarity of conditions of formation over an extended period of time, probably hundreds or thousands of years. A wider view of the Triassic environment is in the next issue of the Journal.

Walk on, using the coast path, for 1¾ km, to where the cliff turns east and Whitehaven comes into view.

TILTED BEDS

Loc. **C4**, NX 942 148, the cliff face you can see across a small gully.

North ←   South →

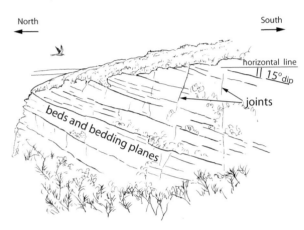

*Fig. C4. The cliff shows tilted Triassic sandstones. The amount of tilt is called the **dip** – in this case 15° to the south. We explain how rocks get tilted in Journal 2.*

The next location is ¾ km ahead, in a field fenced off from the cliff top.

ERRATIC BOULDERS

Loc. **C5**, NX 949 151. (It is not necessary to find the exact location, as you will see plenty more boulders like these).

Fig. C5. Two boulders lying near the top of the cliff. They are very hard (try scratching them !).

The boulders are smoothly rounded, showing that they have been worn by erosion and must have travelled some distance. They are rocks from the central Lake District and were transported to here by a glacier during the final stages of the Ice Age, about 10,000 years ago. They are erratics, that is, boulders that belong to the superficial geology, and not derived directly from the local bedrock – the red sandstones.

Walk on along the coast path for ¾ km.

ROCKS OF ECONOMIC VALUE

Loc. **C6**, NX 956 154, a working quarry at the top of the cliff. Here we return to the Triassic bedrock.

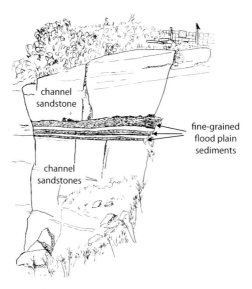

*Fig. **C6**. Part of the north (seaward) wall of the quarry. The thick red sandstones were deposited in river channels (much wider than the width of the exposure) in the Triassic desert. The thin fine–grained layers are muddy sediments from river **floodplains**. The thickness and uniformity of the sandstones make them ideal for use as building stone.*

Out of sight at the base of the cliff there is the disused mine entrance to gypsum deposits below the red sandstones. (Gypsum is a mineral mainly used for making plaster.) **Coal** was extracted from rocks of Carboniferous age at Whitehaven; the mines were worked below the seabed and extended for up to 8 km to the north and west of where you are standing.

11

Winding headgear at the Haig Colliery Mining Museum in Whitehaven.

Almost every rock–type is potentially of economic value, though its commercial importance depends on factors such as the quantity available, the costs of extraction and transport, and the demand for the resource.

The next Location is 4 km ahead. The Route crosses the gently undulating surface of the superficial deposits left behind after the melting of the glaciers, covering the red Triassic sandstones of the bedrock.

Walk along the road into Sandwith, where you turn left. At the end of the village bear right and uphill. Follow the road up to a T–junction and then into the green lane opposite. This leads through Demesne Farm to the B5345 from St Bees to Whitehaven. Cross the road into another farm road; on a clear day there is a panorama of the Lake District:

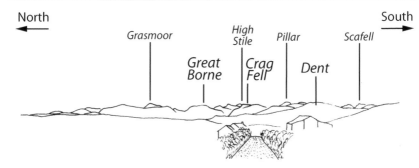

The Coast–to–Coast Route goes over the top of Dent, and then between Crag Fell and Great Borne into Ennerdale.

Follow the road for 600 metres and, beyond the houses, follow the footpath, which forks downhill to the left. Stop on the far side of the railway bridge at any point where you get a clear view to the right (southwest).

A BEDROCK BOUNDARY AND A POST–GLACIAL VALLEY

Loc. **C7**, NX 985 142, on the flat ground near Stanley Pond.

Southeast ←   St Bees   Northwest →

*Fig. **C7**. View southwest down the valley of Pow Beck.
The tower of St Bees Priory church is just visible in the distance.*

The flat floor of the valley is here 17 metres above sea level. The bedrock is 50 metres below you or about 30 metres below sea level. Sea level was lower during the Ice Age than it is now because so much water from the oceans was frozen as glaciers and ice–caps. After the end of the Ice Age the valley was filled with river deposits.

All the way from St Bees the bedrock has been desert sandstones of the Triassic, about 240 million years old. As we cross the valley of Pow Beck, the bedrock changes to humid–tropical rocks of the Carboniferous, about 310 million years old. One would really like to see how the change shows in the rocks but, as with many significant bedrock boundaries, this one is covered by superficial deposits. However, the different bedrock is clear in the change of land use from agricultural to industrial. For the next 4 km we walk through towns whose location is based on the mining of coal from the rocks of the Carboniferous.

Continue on the footpath across the meadows, keeping to the left of the trees. At a bridge under a disused railway, walk on into a lane that leads to the busy A595. Cross to the road opposite into Moor Row. At the town centre turn right on the road to Egremont and after ½ km take the footpath to the left to Cleator. At the T–junction with the A5086 turn left and then next right to Blackhow Bridge.

Blackhow Bridge across the River Ehen marks the end of the first (west Coast) section of the Walk. On the far side of the bridge there is a complete change in the kinds of rock and scenery. So at this point a rather large issue of the Journal summarizes what we have seen so far; the second part is an introduction to the very distinctive features of the Lake District.

JOURNAL 2 – CLEATOR

SEDIMENTARY ROCKS AND ROCK LAYERS (Loc. C3)

The red Triassic sandstones are typical **sedimentary** rocks, deposited as layers at the surface of the Earth. It is probably intuitively obvious that in a sequence of layers the youngest is at the top. It may not be quite so obvious that individual layers are likely to continue for long distances sideways. As a general proposition, most sedimentary rocks are deposited on a nearly horizontal surface, whether on the sea floor or, as with these sandstones, on a low–lying land surface. Many sedimentary units can be traced for tens or hundreds of kilometres.

THE TRIASSIC ENVIRONMENT (Locs. C2, C3, C6)

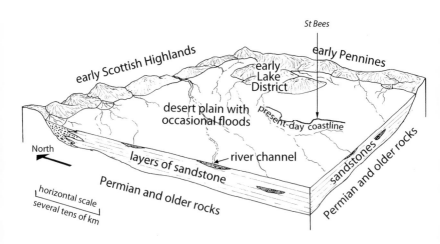

An impression of how the Triassic land surface of northwest England might have looked about 240 million years ago. The mountains of Scotland, the Pennines, and the Lake District had already been formed, and were surrounded by a broad desert plain. Occasional streams and rivers deposited sandstones on the low ground and on the area which is now the Irish Sea.

FOLDED ROCKS (Loc. C4)

You might well think that because the layers you saw at first were near–enough horizontal, they were formed where you now see them. However, as we turned the corner at the northwestern tip of St Bees Head we saw the same kind of rocks, but tilted. The evidence was obvious, but what about the interpretation? We need to think of a sequence of processes, which we can illustrate diagrammatically:

1.

Stage 1. The rocks were deposited as horizontal layers from streams and rivers. Later processes changed the loose sands into hard sandstones.

2.

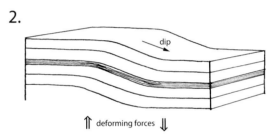

Stage 2. The rocks were covered by younger sediments (perhaps several kilometres thick). While deeply buried the rocks were deformed by large–scale Earth movements.

3.

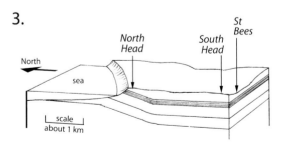

Stage 3. (The present–day scene.) The rocks were gradually raised back to the surface of the Earth and the cover of younger rocks was eroded. The eroded material was deposited as sediments somewhere else.

We will not usually stress this point, but remember that every time you see rocks (other than very young superficial rocks like boulder clay) exposed at the surface of the Earth they must have gone through three stages:

> Stage 1 – formation;
>
> Stage 2 – burial and deformation;
>
> Stage 3 – uplift and erosion.

We are already making history! We need at least three distinct geological episodes, occurring at three different spans of time – each with different environmental conditions – just to account for some rocks that have been tilted.

Earth processes are sometimes described as "the hashing, bashing, and mashing of rocks". All rocks, other than the very youngest, have at some time in their history been covered by a thick pile of younger rocks. It is true that finding marine fossils at the top of a mountain is evidence that the sea at one time covered the area. But how that came about involves a sequence of processes, with dramatic changes in the geography of land and sea, mountains and lowlands. In the long slow story of the formation of our country the whole pattern of continents and oceans has changed almost beyond recognition. It is the fascinating task of the geologist to read back through the evidence of the rocks to disentangle and understand that history.

HOW GEOLOGISTS LOOK AT ROCKS AND SCENERY

The Walk from St Bees to Cleator has illustrated some of the varied fields of geological study – sediments, structures, rocks of economic value, superficial rocks and scenery. We have also seen that essential evidence is often missing – it can be eroded away, or be covered by younger rocks or by vegetation. The task of the geologist is not always straightforward.

It's useful to keep in mind that working in geology is like being a detective. Rocks are the products of processes; we see the products (the scene of crime, so to speak) but have to infer the processes (the perpetrators – the agents of erosion and deposition, Earth movements, and many other kinds of activity – which left the scene millions of years ago).

Two powerful questions can be applied to any geological situation:

- *"What does this rock (or fossil, or structure, or scenery) tell us about what was going on in the Earth at the time it was being made?"*

- *"And what has happened to it since?"*

To answer such questions we need a variety of methods for thinking about space and time, sometimes outside the familiar box of everyday shapes and events.

- The scale of space varies from fine detail (like the shape of a layer in a sequence of sediments) to tens or hundreds of kilometres (like an overview of the whole of the Lake District or the hidden deep structure of the upper layers of the Earth). We shall often need to think about rocks far below the Earth's surface, and sometimes about rocks, no longer present, which have been eroded away from above the surface.

- The scale of time varies from the duration of a single episode (like the formation of a sedimentary layer – maybe as short as a few weeks or months) up to hundreds of millions of years (like the slow drift of continents over the surface of the Earth).

- The landscape around you gives an overview of the environment as it is now – St Bees sea–front is a good example. The clues to understanding landscapes of the past are revealed in rocks, most often in sequences of layers formed over a span of time – as in the cliffs of St Bees Head.

- Usually no single exposure or view contains all the information we need to answer the questions posed above. Like a detective solving a case, we shall often have to refer back, or wait for more evidence to arrive, before framing an answer. The delay in completing an explanation is more than compensated by letting you find out about rocks and scenery from your own observations.

- Since there were no human witnesses to the geological history, the answers to our questions are nearly always provisional. In effect, you are judge and jury, deciding whether our explanations are reasonable. You can also be the detective and search for more evidence to support or refute the case. New evidence often challenges what we thought we knew before.

MILLIONS OF YEARS

We shall often need to speak of millions, especially of years. A million is difficult to visualise, but some images might help. A table–tennis ball is 40 millimetres in diameter and weighs 2.7 grams. A million of them would make a cube with sides 4 metres long (about twice the volume of an average room) and would weigh 2.7 tonnes.

If you counted the balls at the rate of one a second, without stopping for food or sleep, it would take you eleven and a half days.

In human terms, there are fewer than a thousand generations between us and the people of the Stone Age. A million generations would take us far back to our mammalian ancestors in the Tertiary era (see the chart in Journal **1**).

Alternatively you could just think of a million as a very large number and concentrate on the numbers of them. So, for instance, we shall shortly be thinking about dates of 470 and 452 million years ago, 18 million years apart. Whilst 18 is a small number, 18 million years is a very long time.

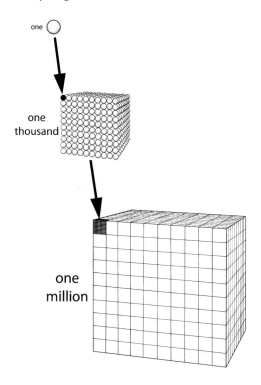

PLATE TECTONICS

Rocks and scenery of past geological time are best understood in the context of global changes in geography. The final chapter of the book summarises the development of northern England with a sequence of plate–tectonic maps. You could look at them at intervals during the Walk; some are reproduced here as a preview:

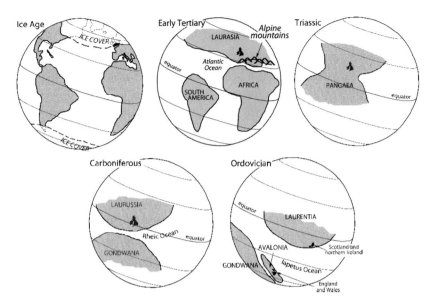

Plate–tectonic reconstructions of past positions of continents and oceans.

INTRODUCTION TO THE LAKE DISTRICT

LOWER PALAEOZOIC

Age range: 542–416 million years ago

Latitude of the Lake District: approx. 30°S

Climate: temperate

The rocks of the Lake District are of Lower Palaeozoic age (Ordovician and Silurian – see the chart in the Introduction). The next 80 km of the Walk, from the River Ehen to Shap Abbey, crosses only Ordovician rocks, but what we shall see is representative of the Lake District as a whole. The rocks are much older than anything we have seen so far and they have a more complex history. The questions:

- "What does this rock tell us about what was going on in the Earth at the time it was being made?"

- "And what has happened to it since?"

will take more teasing apart to answer but will also reveal more about how the Earth works. (To continue the detective analogy from earlier in Journal **2**, it's as though the scene of crime has been trampled over by other culprits before we get to see it.) The questions, and the answers, will be literally at a deeper level because we shall be dealing with processes deep within the crust of the Earth as well as at its surface.

For the first 12 km of the Walk east of Cleator the bedrocks are **mudstones** (fine–grained rocks which were originally deep–sea muds and are much tougher than their name implies). A **granite** occupies the western half of Ennerdale. The bedrock for the next 70 km of the Walk, as far as Shap Abbey, is almost entirely hard **volcanic** rocks, making the highest mountains of the Lake District.

ROCKS FORMED FROM LIQUID MAGMA: DIFFERENT PROCESSES, DIFFERENT PRODUCTS

Igneous rocks are formed from liquid **magma** in two ways: by being erupted at the Earth's surface (extrusive or **volcanic** rocks) or by cooling and solidifying within the Earth's **crust** (**intrusive** rocks). The two overlap a bit, as we shall see.

VOLCANIC ROCKS

Volcanic rocks are not the easiest to understand because of the variety of different processes that can make them. And in the Lake District an episode of **mountain–building** has changed their appearance substantially. We'll introduce the different volcanic rock types as we encounter clear examples of each.

Volcanic rocks can be **erupted** in a variety of ways, from the relatively gentle oozing out of lava to the cataclysmically explosive. The appearance of a volcanic rock depends on the way in which it was erupted. Some of the different kinds of volcano are shown in the next drawing. The Table lists the characteristics of some common volcanic rock–types.

Drawing	Process	Analogy	Rock	Typical features
	Eruption			
a	Lava flow	Thick treacle	**Lava**	Homogeneous, unlayered, composed of fine crystals
b	Ash fall	Spray–can	**Bedded tuff**	Layered, largely grains (frozen droplets); can fall on land or into water
c	Ash flow	Paint–ball gun	**Welded tuff**	Lozenges formed from flattened droplets, giving a streaky structure
a	Near–surface intrusion (the volcano's plumbing)	Thick treacle squeezed along a crack	**Dyke or sill**	As lava, but margins may be finer–grained than centre. Dyke margins cut across layering; sills parallel it
	Reworking			
not shown	Gravity fall	Landslide	**Breccia**	Unlayered, composed of blocks of varying size
not shown	Flowing water	Stream crossing a sand beach	**Reworked tuff**	Finely layered, size–sorted, with sedimentary structures

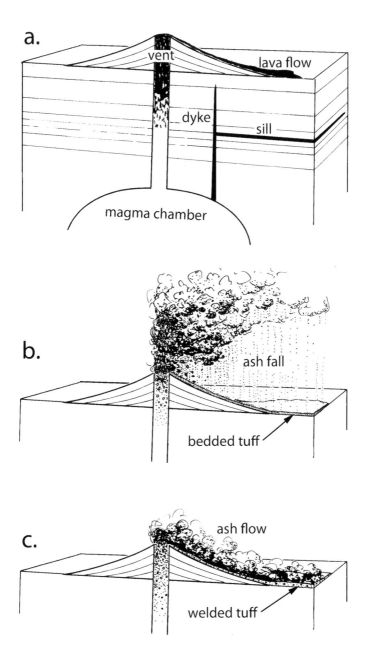

The main ways in which volcanic rocks are formed

As the Table suggests, volcanic rocks can vary a lot, and it may not be possible to determine a volcanic rock's origin from its appearance in the field. We shall comment in more detail as we come across examples.

Here are a few remarks on the big picture. Volcanoes are very large structures – much bigger than can be understood at individual locations. The volcanoes which produced the volcanic rocks that we shall see were part of a set of volcanoes strung out along the edge of an ancient continent. We return to this in Journal **4**. The summits of the Lake District volcanoes have long since been eroded away; what we see today are their eroded remnants and parts of the internal plumbing. As you may imagine, the way these various bits fit together will be a good deal more complex than the sort of layer–cake arrangement of the sandstones seen at St Bees. We may not always be able to unscramble the relationships, but we'll point out places where they are clear.

Over much of the central Lake District the rocks are very well exposed and in places you may see some types that we will not describe till later. As with all rocks on the Walk, if the weather is dull or wet you may see less detail than we describe.

INTRUSIVE ROCKS

Not all magmas reach the surface. Some, like dykes and sills (Fig. a, on previous page), get close to the surface and form parts of a volcano's plumbing. Others solidify at greater depth as larger bodies several kilometres across. The only one we shall see is **granite** (Loc. **L10**).

Most granite magmas form by the melting of rocks tens of kilometres below the surface. The magma has a low density compared with solid rocks and so rises through the crust (with a shape and movement rather like the action of a lava lamp – see the drawing on the next page). When it gets too cool, and consequently too sticky to rise any further, it solidifies at temperatures of 600–700°C. This is usually at a relatively shallow depth – perhaps 2–5 km. As the granite cools, its heat spreads into and bakes the surrounding rocks. The process is called **thermal metamorphism**; a familiar analogue is the manufacture of bricks from clay.

When you see a granite exposed at the surface, remember that at the time it was intruded it was covered by several kilometres of rock, since eroded away. The entire Lake District section of the Walk is underlain by granite, but most is buried beneath other rocks.

depth at
time of
intrusion

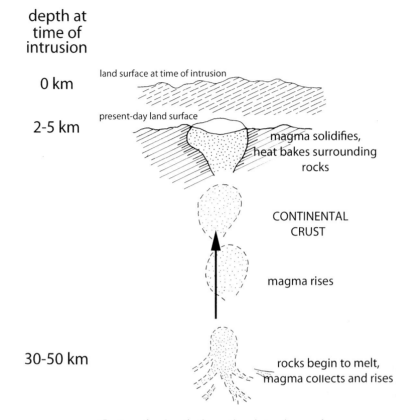

Cartoon showing the formation, intrusion, and
solidification of granite magma.

DEFORMED ROCKS AND CLEAVAGE

The Lake District rocks have been much more deeply buried, to about 5–10 km,
than the Triassic rocks we saw in the coastal region. At these depths temperatures
are 150–300°C and pressures are 1500–3000 times greater than at the surface of the
Earth. Rocks originally formed at the surface become much easier to deform. When
they are compressed they develop new structures which overprint or even destroy
sedimentary features like fossils and bedding. The structure you will see most often
on the Walk is **cleavage**, explained below.

A ROCK BEFORE COMPRESSION

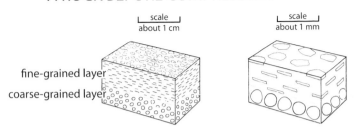

fine-grained layer
coarse-grained layer

THE SAME ROCK AFTER COMPRESSION

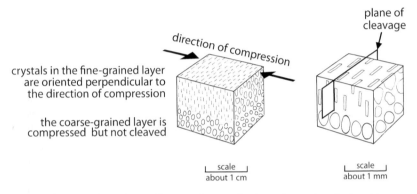

plane of cleavage

direction of compression

crystals in the fine-grained layer
are oriented perpendicular to
the direction of compression

the coarse-grained layer is
compressed but not cleaved

When first formed as sediments, fine–grained muds are deposited as tiny flat grains; coarser sandy layers are made of more–rounded grains (upper drawings). When rocks are compressed (lower drawings), fine–grained layers develop a new structure of microscopic disc–shaped crystals oriented at right angles to the direction of compression. A similar principle applies to fine–grained volcanic products like ash. In coarser layers the grains respond to the compression by being squashed, but without other changes.

Cleavage forms only in rocks that are fine–grained, like mudstones (Loc. **L6**) or volcanic ash and tuff (e.g. Loc. **L22**). The well–organised alignment of the crystals makes it easy to split the rock parallel to the cleavage. Where the cleavage is particularly well–developed, as at Loc. **L22**, the rock becomes a slate, usable for roofing.

ROCK COLOUR

Probably the first thing that one notices about a rock is its colour. A rock's colour is caused by the minerals that compose it and the way in which light is reflected off them. So, in principle, colour should be a guide to mineral content and thus to rock–type. Unfortunately there are other factors at work, and they particularly affect the outer surface of a rock. They are: weathering, staining by groundwaters, lichen covering, and also a rock's grain size.

Volcanic rocks such as those found in the Lake District are most commonly grey when freshly formed. This may seem dull, but it means that a grey rock is most likely to have been relatively unaffected by weathering. The most obvious products of weathering, oxides of iron, have bright and distinctive colours – mostly shades of red, brown, orange, and yellow – and groundwaters most commonly stain rocks a reddish brown colour. The surest way to check if a rock is fresh is to break it apart with a hammer – something that most walkers will not wish to carry – or to look for corners or edges already broken open by earlier visitors.

Clearly we need to use colour with caution. A useful guideline is to look at the colour boundaries. Weathering and staining tend to vary gradually across a rock, so they produce *gradational* boundaries. If a colour boundary is *sharp* it is likely to be due to an original feature of the rock – not something that has happened to it since it formed.

THE SCENERY OF THE LAKE DISTRICT

The Lake District is renowned for its dramatic scenery, richly expressed by artists and writers. It may seem prosaic to say that the scenery is largely an outcome of the Ice Age, but awareness of the dynamic processes going on in the landscape may add to the feeling of drama. The flow of ice sheets and glaciers made the big pattern of the major valleys. The fine details have mostly been created by erosion and deposition during rapid global warming from about 12,000 to 10,000 years ago, continued at a more sedate pace up to the present day. The scenery has been further modified (increasingly in the last few hundred years) by human influence.

The complexity of today's scenery is the outcome of a sequence of varied processes crammed into the last few thousand years. It is a landscape out of equilibrium, in the sense that it is still changing. It looks very different now from how it was 10,000 years ago or what it will be like 10,000 years into the future.

2. THE LAKE DISTRICT

At the River Ehen we move abruptly from Triassic and Carboniferous (360 to 200 million years old) on to the much older Ordovician and Silurian (490 to 420 million years), which underlie the whole of the Lake District. The bedrock for much of the Walk after the first 20 km is a great thickness and variety of volcanic rocks, which give an insight into how volcanoes develop. The magnificent mountain and valley scenery was carved by glaciers during the (much more recent) Ice Age.

THE WALK – CLEATOR TO ROSTHWAITE

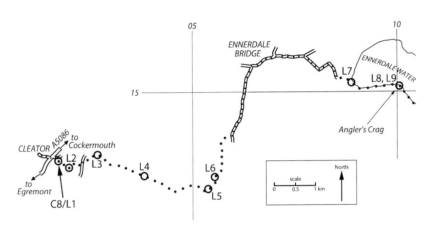

Cleator to Ennerdale Water.

Loc. **C8/L1**, NY 017 134. Blackhow Bridge over the River Ehen is the "gateway to Lakeland" in terms of rocks and scenery as much as it is for industry, population, and land use.

Once again, boulder clay and alluvium (superficial deposits) cover an important boundary in the underlying bedrock. We must leave an account of what it is like until we get to the far side of the Lake District. For the present, we can note:

- The terrain changes from the gentle slopes of the coastal area to the bigger and steeper hills of the Lake District.

- From here all the way to the east coast at Robin Hood's Bay the general pattern is for the bedrock to get progressively younger. As we continue the Walk we shall be working out the history of the last 500 million years in northern England.

Continue on the track for ½ km. The next Location is the flat surface of the track 10 metres before the sharp left bend.

27

A FIRST SIGHT OF MUDSTONES

Loc. **L2**, NY 019 132. Ordovician mudstones, about 470 million years old, are exposed for a few metres on the surface of the track. They are worth a brief look as our first encounter with these rocks, but we shall see them much better at the next Location.

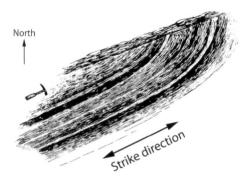

*Fig. **L2**. The bedding of the mudstones shows as variations in shades of grey on the flat surface of the track. A small fold and a disturbance at the top of the drawing give a hint of the structural complexity we shall see later. The general direction of the **strike** (the compass direction of the bedding planes on a horizontal surface) is NE-SW – a direction which is persistent throughout the Lake District.*

Continue along the track. When you reach the tarmac road at Black How Farm take the gated forestry track up to a right-hand bend. Total distance from the last Location is 1 km.

DEEP-SEA SEDIMENTS

Loc. **L3**, NY 026 135, a shallow quarry beside the bend of the track in Blackhow Wood. The rocks are Ordovician mudstones, as at the last Location. Look at clean faces of a few loose fragments; they show bedding on a much finer scale than you saw earlier in the Triassic sandstones.

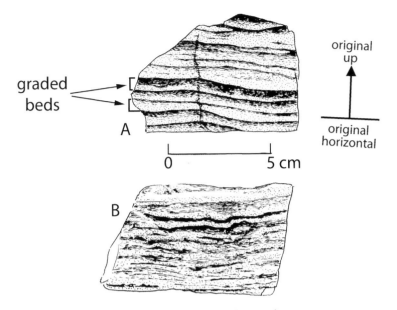

*Fig. L3. Two pieces of Ordovician mudstone,
with alternating light and dark layers.*

In **A** the light (coarser) layers grade upwards into the dark (finer) layers – the pattern that results from a mix of grain sizes settling out in still water; each coarse-to-fine unit represents one episode of deposition. (You can easily reproduce the effect by stirring a mix of mud and sand in a glass of water. The sand settles in a few minutes; the mud may take several days.) This kind of sedimentary structure can be used for working out the original orientation ("way-up") of the sediments, as labelled in the drawing.

In **B** the same grading from coarse to fine layering is present but it is more disorganised – the result of movement of the sediment while it was still soft.

These rocks are very different from the Triassic sandstones on the coast. They were made in a deep-sea environment, with individual **graded beds** deposited from a suspension of particles varying in size from coarse to fine. Such suspensions were carried into the otherwise stagnant environment by intermittent flows of turbid water.

Continue along the track and footpath to the summit of Dent (1 km).

The stones in the wall beside the path change from rounded glacial erratics to very angular shapes, which are the characteristic joint pattern of an igneous rock. This is the first **igneous** rock we have seen, and we shall see many more further on in the Walk. What you do not see is the bedrock of Ordovician mudstone, even though it forms the whole of the hill.

A HILL WITH A VIEW

Loc. **L4**, NY 038 131. On a fine day there are superb views from the summit of Dent. As Alfred Wainwright says, the whole of the west Cumbrian coastal plain is seen "as on a map". It gives us an opportunity to see how the area fits into a wider context.

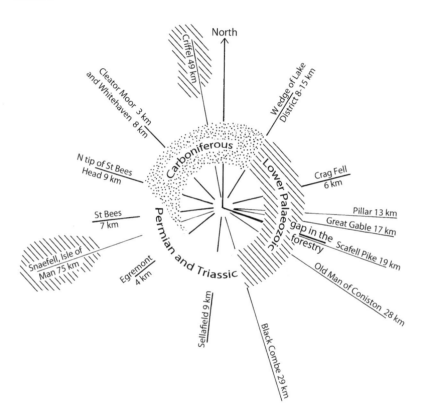

Fig. L4/1. Showing a 360° panorama from the top of Dent, with distances to some landmarks and an indication of the bedrock geology. If you are standing at the eastern summit, the prominent gap in the forestry 2 km to the east is helpful for orientating the drawing.

You may wish to start by tracing your route from St Bees, almost due west, and the first steps of the Walk round St Bees Head on the rocks of the Triassic. The older rocks of the Carboniferous, with its coal-mining towns, extend from west to north. The still older Lower Palaeozoic rocks of the Lake District rise abruptly from below the Carboniferous in the northeast and fill all the view from northeast to south. The Triassic occupies the coastal area from south to west. It underlies largely agricultural land, apart from the nuclear reprocessing plant of Sellafield to the south.

If you are fortunate enough to have very clear views, you may be able to see the Isle of Man to the west and Criffel (and perhaps even Cairnsmore of Fleet) in southern Scotland to the north. The bedrock of both areas is Lower Palaeozoic – the same rocks as in the Lake District. The Solway Firth (Fig. **L4/2**) lies between England and Scotland – it marks a geologically significant line, as will become apparent further on in the Walk.

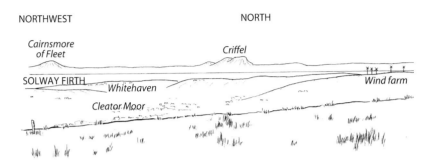

*Fig. **L4/2**. View north from the top of Dent. The heights of the Scottish hills are exaggerated.*

The next part of the Walk trends northeast from Dent and passes on the north side of Crag Fell (marked on Fig. **L4/1**).

> *When you have completed your survey (sooner if it's cold and wet), walk on for another 2 km. The Route follows the path to join a track beside a plantation. Where the track comes to a deer fence, cross by the tall stile and use the path down into Uldale. As you descend from Dent, views of Nannycatch Beck and its tributaries open out.*

A CHARMING NAME, A CHARMING VALLEY, A HECTIC HISTORY

Loc. **L5**, NY 053 127, on the final stage of the descent, or any convenient viewpoint.

Fig. L5. Looking north up Nannycatch Beck.

In its steep-sided valley Nannycatch Beck is an example of a **misfit** – a stream which is now too small to have eroded the valley it occupies. The valley was cut at the end of the Ice Age when rapid global warming melted the glaciers, producing vast quantities of water, either overflowing from ice-dammed lakes or as streams flowing beneath the glaciers. (Try to imagine the power of a stream which could erode so much tough bedrock in a relatively short time – probably only a few years.) The flat bottom of the valley is the result of recent deposition following after the rapid erosion.

The cross-section of the valley is markedly **V**-shaped, typical of erosion by flowing water. We shall contrast this with the ice-carved **U**-shapes of the valleys of Central Lakeland.

Walk down into the valley and then up it, to the north, for ½ km. The prominent crags on the west side (Raven Crag) are formed by an exposure of a fine-grained igneous rock intruded into the Ordovician mudstones as a vertical sheet about 50 metres thick. The next Location is immediately north of the gate across the path.

BEDDING AND CLEAVAGE

Loc. **L6**, NY 056 130. This big exposure of Ordovician mudstone shows a rock structure we have not previously seen – **cleavage**. It's worth spending a few minutes here, as cleavage will be a major feature of all the strongly deformed rocks for the next 75 km.

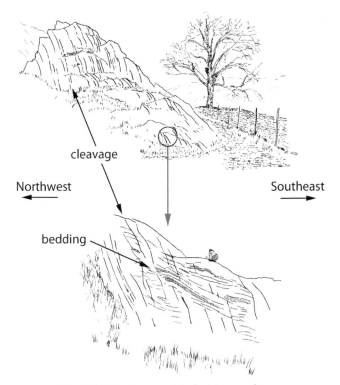

Northwest ⟵

Southeast ⟶

cleavage

bedding

*Fig. L6. The exposure of Ordovician mudstones
on the north side of Nannycatch gate.*

The top drawing shows the whole exposure. The dominant structure is the **cleavage**, dipping at 70° to the right (southeast).

The lower drawing shows the detail of the lowest part of the exposure nearest to the gate. Look closely to see the fine-scale banding – the original bedding – dipping at 20° to the right. The **strike** of the cleavage is NE-SW (parallel to the path, and the same as where we first saw the mudstones). The cleavage is perpendicular to the direction of compression (Journal **2**) – this was NW-SE in all the Lower Palaeozoic rocks of the Lake District.

Continue to the north end of the valley (1 km). Where you climb out to the east there is an exposure (NY 059 140) of the Ordovician mudstones. Take note of their general appearance, or even find a small chip to take with you, because the next time we see these rocks (4 km ahead) they will look very different.

Continue along the road to Ennerdale Bridge. At the centre of the village take the right fork, and at the road junction ¾ km ahead turn right again. At the car park at the end of the tarmac road there is a footpath through the wood to the south side of Ennerdale Water. All the way from the climb out of the Nannycatch valley the ground is covered by boulder clay.

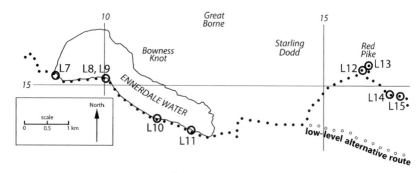

Ennerdale Water to Red Pike.

ALLUVIAL FAN

Loc. **L7**, NY 089 152, at the west end of Ennerdale Water. The lake is naturally dammed by boulder clay and the level has been slightly raised by the man-made weir.

*Fig. L7. The large **alluvial fan** at the foot of Ben Gill on the south side of Ennerdale. Work is in progress on the water flow in Ben Gill and the River Ehen below the weir to protect endangered freshwater pearl mussels which live in the river.*

Continue for 1 km along the south shore of the lake.

BAKED MUDSTONES

Loc. **L8**, NY 100 151, on the west side of Angler's Crag. The rocks here are an exception (for a good reason) to the earlier statement that cleavage is often a dominant feature of the Lake District rocks.

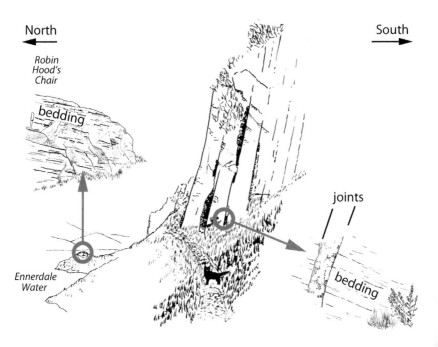

*Fig. **L8/1**. The cliff on the west side of Angler's Crag.*

At first sight the prominent "chimney" features look as though they might be thick sedimentary beds. But they lack the internal layering that we've seen in rocks like those at St Bees Head. The real bedding shows on Robin Hood's Chair – the knob of rock on the north side of the path (Fig. **L8/1**, inset). There the fine layers show as parallel ribs and grooves, particularly clear on the north side. This bedding dips gently to the south – exactly as it does in the Ordovician mudstones at Nannycatch (Loc. **L6**). So the "chimneys" are a different feature – joints – which provide no useful information.

At Nannycatch the rocks are relatively soft and have obvious cleavage. Here they are hard and have no discernible cleavage. The reason the rocks are so different is that the Ordovician mudstones here have been heated by a large body of **granite**. The granite is 5 km across, and we are about 300 metres away from its western margin, on the other side of Angler's Crag. When intruded into the mudstones the temperature of the granite would have been 600-700°C. The mudstones were baked (**thermally metamorphosed** – Journal **2**), hardening the rock and nearly destroying original structures like bedding and cleavage. The prominence of Angler's Crag, and of Bowness Knot on the opposite side of Ennerdale Water, is due to the toughness of these baked rocks.

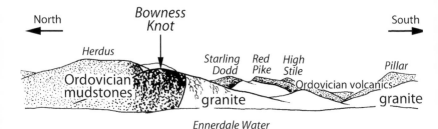

Fig. L8/2. The boundary between the granite and the Ordovician rocks runs through the crags on Bowness Knot. Further east the roof of the granite appears on Starling Dodd and Red Pike.

The next Location is 20 metres ahead. Be careful to stay on the path, scrambling up through the crags and avoiding the dangerous steep face below.

GRANITE

Loc. **L9**, NY 100 151, in the first part of the scramble past Angler's Crag.

In places the rock in the path is white – much paler than the grey mudstone. The contacts (or boundaries) between the two are sharp, but irregular. The white rock is a fine-grained version of the granite that we shall see shortly. It's a **dyke** caused by magma squeezing through cracks in the rock that surrounded the cooling **granite** mass (see Journal **2**, Volcanic Rocks, Drawing a).

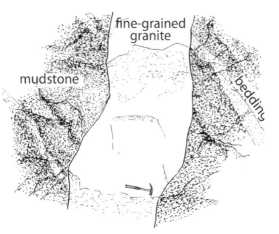

Fig. **L9**. Granite dyke cutting across the indistinct bedding of the mudstones.

Continue along the south side of Ennerdale Water. Within the next 100 metres you cross from the Ordovician mudstones onto the Ennerdale Granite. The contact is not exposed, though the many loose boulders of coarse-grained pink granite hint at the change of bedrock. We shall see the granite in place at the lake side 1 km ahead.

Loc. **L10**, NY 112(0) 142(8), 200 metres east of the gate by Red Beck, and 25 metres east of a small stream crossed by stepping stones. Where the path comes down to the lake shore there is a small exposure of the Ennerdale Granite. It's easily missed, so keep looking at the rocks at the water's edge as you walk along. The exposure is particularly clean and free of vegetation because it is washed by the waters of the lake.

Small exposures of bedrock surrounded by pebbles can be hard to distinguish from loose boulders. Here the clue is that the granite looks as though it is rooted in the gravelly shore rather than resting on top of it.

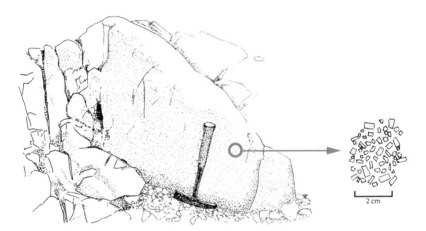

Fig. L10/1. Exposure of the Ennerdale Granite on the lake shore.

The granite was intruded as a liquid (**magma**) at 600-700°C into the Ordovician mudstones 452 million years ago. The homogeneous appearance and the lack of bedding are typical of an igneous rock solidified from a liquid. The *inset* shows a freshly broken surface of the granite, made of angular **feldspar** crystals surrounded by much smaller crystals (not illustrated). The granite here solidified while it was covered by several kilometres thickness of Ordovician rock. The age of the mudstones is 470 million years but, as we shall see, a lot happened in the time between the deposition of the original muds and the intrusion of the granite.

The Ennerdale Granite has been suggested as a possible site for the deep storage of radioactive waste. The presumed advantage is that the rock at depth would have fewer joints than many other rock-types and would be relatively easy to seal to prevent escape of stored materials.

AN ICE-CARVED VALLEY

From the same Location there is a good view up Ennerdale.

Fig. L10/2. The valley has the typical shape resulting from glacial erosion – nearly straight or gently curved along its length, and U-shaped in its cross-section.

Continue along the lakeside for a further 1 km.

RECENT SEDIMENTS IN THE GLACIAL VALLEY

Loc. **L11**, NY 120 140, or any convenient stopping point with a view to the top of the lake.

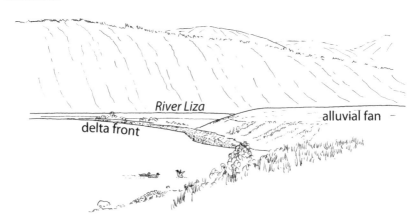

Fig. L11. The top end of Ennerdale Water from the south.

The floodplain of the River Liza in the main valley was deposited as an advancing **delta**; the delta front forms most of the shoreline at the top end of the lake. An alluvial fan from a tributary to the right (Woundell Beck) makes the terrace-like feature. These flat features cover the floor of the original **U**-shaped glacial valley.

It is helpful to have some idea of the scale and rates of geological processes (how big, how much, how fast, how slow). The top end of Ennerdale valley provides a self-contained example for making some simple calculations, based on the date of about 10,000 years ago for the melting of the glacier which formerly occupied the valley. You could think about what more you would need to know, and what assumptions to make, so as to guess at, for instance, the amount of rock eroded and then deposited in the valley since the end of the Ice Age. We present some estimates of useful numbers in Journal **3**.

Leaving the lake end take the path east. In 300 metres turn left and follow the north edge of the forestry plantation. In a further 300 metres turn left on a track that emerges from the forest and head north across pasture to a bridge across the River Liza. Cross the bridge, turn right, and follow the track for 1½ km, passing High Gillerthwaite Youth Hostel, to a cattle grid where the track enters the forestry (NY 146 141). Here there is a choice of routes.

To follow the low-level route (see the map below), cross the cattle grid and follow the track through the forest to Black Sail Hut (NY 195 124). Continue ESE for ¾ km to the ravine of Loft Beck, where you strike off left up the hillside on the west side of the beck. (Do not stay on the main path, which leads to Great Gable.) In ¾ km the slope lessens and the path bends eastwards, following a cairned route that skirts Brandreth on your right. West of Grey Knotts the path turns north and descends in a straight line to the old tramway at NY 216 135. Here the path joins the high-level route, described below. Turn sharp right and follow the tramway to Honister.

We have chosen to describe Wainwright's "high-level alternative" for four reasons: it crosses a greater and more representative variety of rocks, the rocks are much better exposed, they give an insight into how volcanoes work, and the route offers better views of the structure and scenery. It is 2 km to the next Location.

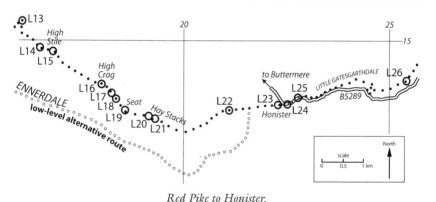

Red Pike to Honister.

At the cattle grid (NY 146 141) turn left and follow the path climbing between blocks of forestry and then over grassy hillsides with little rock exposure. Cross the two branches of Gillflinter Beck and follow a line of cairns northeastwards towards Red Pike, noting rounded pink granite boulders on the hillside.

THE TOP OF THE GRANITE

Loc. **L12**, NY 159 154, about 120 metres southwest of Red Pike. Close to Red Pike's summit a line of metal fence posts comes into view. About 50 metres before you reach them the granite boulders give way to more angular ones of a grey rock – evidence of a change in the underlying bedrock.

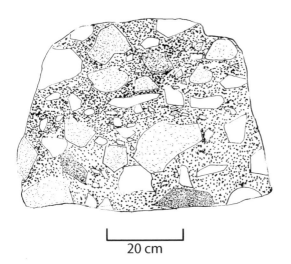

*Fig. **L12**. Example of breccia, a mishmash of fragments of varying size and shape in a finer-grained matrix. The size, appearance, and arrangement of fragments in the breccias on Red Pike vary a lot, so you may not come across a rock exactly like this.*

20 cm

Most of the boulders are covered with lichen, but careful examination of a few should reveal that they are made up of fragments up to 30 cm across, some angular and some rounded. The fragments are enclosed in a matrix of grey finer-grained material, but you should be able to make out the edges of many of them. Such *rocks made of other rocks* are known as **breccias**. Breccias can form in several ways. Possibly these derive from previously erupted materials that have broken up and slid down the side of a volcano under gravity. This explains the variety of shape and size, and the fact that the colours are uniform grey – they are all from the same volcano.

Loc. **L13**, NY 160 154, Red Pike Summit. As you approach the summit cairn, exposures of pale grey breccia give way to a dark grey fine-grained rock with no obvious internal structure. You last saw this rock at Anglers Crag. It is mudstone heated to 300-400°C by the granite which is here 10 metres or so below your feet. In fact you have climbed up through the granite body and have emerged in the overlying rocks. You will be able to view the relationship in 3D shortly.

We need to emphasise here that the breccias and mudstones were already in place and solid when the granite was intruded (see "Intrusive Rocks" in Journal **2**). Where we are standing is very close to the roof of the granite – the point where it stopped moving and solidified. A few million more years from now erosion will have removed all the overlying rock, leaving only the granite visible.

From Red Pike follow the path eastward along the crest of the broad ridge over exposures of breccia of varying appearance. There are six Locations between here and Haystacks – total distance 4 km along the ridge.

Loc. **L14**, NY 165 148, just before the ascent to High Stile. Pause to look left down a steep gully at Bleaberry Tarn in its glacial corrie and back towards the summit of Red Pike.

The red screes from which Red Pike is named mark the outcrop of granite on the Buttermere side. You are standing on volcanic rocks which overlie it and extend back to Red Pike. The ones on the right of the gully are bedded tuffs, identifiable by the near-horizontal stripes. We shall be able to examine this type of rock shortly.

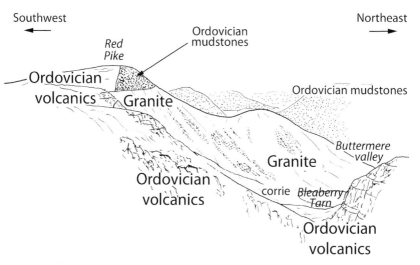

*Fig. **L14/1**. View of Red Pike from the southeast showing the various rocks and their contacts.*

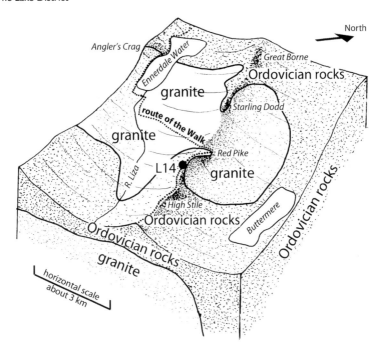

Fig. L14/2. Cartoon of the ridge between Ennerdale and Buttermere showing the three-dimensional shape of the Ennerdale Granite and its contacts with the Ordovician volcanic and sedimentary rocks.

The granite is more easily eroded than the Ordovician rocks so it makes lower ground, with parts of the roof of the granite forming the ridge at Red Pike and Starling Dodd.

CLOUDS OF ASH

The path climbs to High Stile through an assortment of volcanic rocks: largely breccia and tuff. We have seen breccia before. A **tuff** *is a rock formed from frozen droplets of magma (ash) sprayed from a volcano.*

Loc. **L15**, NY 168 148, High Stile summit, and continuing further to the east. Here the exposures of tuff are more or less continuous. We'll start by looking at the size of the ash grains. A useful technique here is to feel the rock with a finger-tip – preferably one without calluses! The rougher the surface, the coarser are the grains. You can see thin layers of sand-sized particles and areas of unlayered coarser-grained material with particles of various shapes up to golf-ball size. In places the two are interlayered. The layering is horizontal, so the tuffs have the same orientation as when they were erupted onto roughly level ground 450 million years ago.

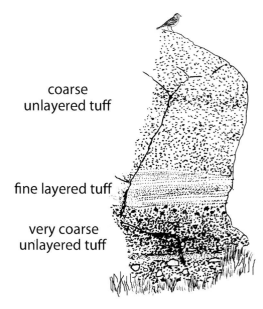

coarse
unlayered tuff

fine layered tuff

very coarse
unlayered tuff

Fig. L15/1.
Interbedded layered
and unlayered tuff,
High Stile summit.

Hereabouts you may see tuffs where some of the layers cut across others. This is
cross-bedding, formed by flowing water – a feature that we saw in sandstones at Loc.
C2. Where streams have moved ash around like this we call the deposits **reworked
tuffs**.

*Fig. L15/2. Reworked
tuffs, showing cross-
bedding.*

The path follows the ridge crest with excellent views north and south.

Note the contrast in scenery between the smooth largely crag-free slopes of the mudstones north of Buttermere to your left and the craggy volcanic rocks on Pillar and neighbouring summits to your right. The boundary between the two rock groups runs along the south side of the Buttermere valley, immediately below the ridge you are standing on.

A VIEWPOINT AND SOME LANDSCAPE INTERPRETATION

Loc. **L16**, NY 180 140, High Crag. This affords an excellent view of the route to the east, passing over Seat and Haystacks, to the south of Fleetwith Pike, and later over Helvellyn.

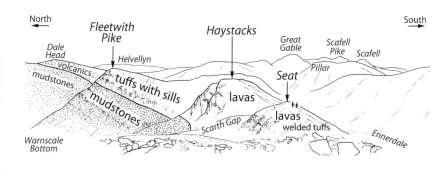

*Fig. L16. View east from High Crag showing
the main rocks close to the route.*

We'll describe most of the rocks as we come across them. There are two that we won't see – mudstones and sills. Warnscale Bottom and the lower slopes of Fleetwith Pike and Dale Head are underlain by mudstones, like the ones we saw at Loc. **L2** – relatively easily weathered so poorly exposed. Overlying them on the craggy upper slopes of Fleetwith Pike are volcanic rocks – tuffs interlayered with **sills**. In good lighting you can pick out three lines of crags, one above the other, sloping gently down to the right parallel to the fell top. These are the sills – formed from magma squeezed between the tuff layers (see the drawing in the Volcanic Rocks section of Journal **2**). The ledges between are underlain by more easily weathered tuffs.

The rocks you can see between High Crag and Scafell on the skyline have a total thickness of at least 3000 metres. This is roughly half the overall thickness of volcanic rocks in the Lake District. Clearly the volcanism 450 million years ago was an important episode in the story of the evolution of Britain. We summarise the history in Journal **4**.

Descend towards Seat.

LAVAS AND GLOWING AVALANCHES

Loc. **L17**, NY 182 139, Gamlin End. As you descend, look out for speckled smooth-surfaced pale grey rocks. These are **lavas** – the first we have seen on the Walk. The brightly reflecting speckles are crystals of **feldspar**, many of them rectangular (brick-shaped in 3D).

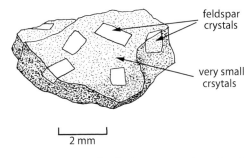

feldspar crystals

very small crsytals

Fig. L17. Lava with crystals, much enlarged.

2 mm

In contrast to the tuffs, the lava is smooth-surfaced. This is because it was erupted as a coherent mass of liquid, and when it solidified it formed a network of interlocking microscopic crystals, with larger ones scattered through it. We explain the two sizes in Journal **3**.

Pause at the saddle between High Crag and Seat.

Loc. **L18**, NY 183 136. The rock exposures a few metres to the left of the path are coarse tuffs, but with a different appearance from those seen up to now. These tuffs contain an abundance of lozenge-shaped pits, formed where large ash particles have weathered more rapidly than the surrounding rock.

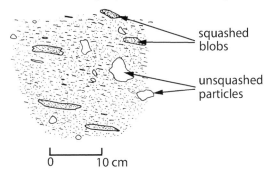

squashed blobs

unsquashed particles

0   10 cm

Fig. L18. Welded tuff. Lozenge shapes are squashed blobs of magma, flattened parallel to the original horizontal. Unsquashed particles were erupted solid. In between are finer particles of ash.

The particles formed from broken pieces of solid rock that were carried down the volcano's slopes in a cloud of very hot gas – an **ash flow** or glowing avalanche. This is the most destructive type of volcanic eruption, like the one that destroyed Pompeii in 79 CE. On deposition the still-liquid blobs were squashed into lozenges and welded into a solid rock. We enlarge on this in Journal **3**.

Locs **L15**, **L17**, and **L18** provide examples of three kinds of volcanic product shown in Journal **2**, Volcanic Rocks – ash fall, lava flow, and ash flow. They also show how it's the fine detail in rocks that provides clues about how the rocks were made.

Climb to the summit of Seat.

Loc. **L19**, NY 186 133. The top of Seat is again made of lava: pale grey and weathering into smooth well-jointed blocks, and without visible crystals such as those we saw on High Crag.

From Seat the view westwards shows the structure of High Crag – tuffs dipping toward the south with lavas underlying them.

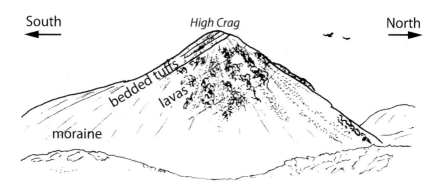

*Fig. **L19/1**. High Crag viewed from Seat, showing the bedded tuffs on the summit with lavas below.*

To the east is Haystacks, composed of a pile of lavas, each producing a crag capped by a ledge.

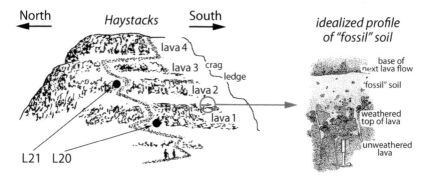

*Fig. **L19/2**. Haystacks from Seat, showing how the tops of lavas form ledges. At least four lavas can be distinguished. The drawing on the right shows the detail of the top of a lava.*

The boundaries between successive lavas weather more rapidly than the interiors, and this produces the ledges. We discuss some intriguing details in the Journal.

From Scarth Gap the path climbs onto Haystacks, starting on lavas, with feldspar crystals.

Loc. **L20**, NY 191 133. The first crag to the right of the path has the usual steeply inclined joints. Also visible are shorter cracks which are nearly horizontal. These are due to the upper parts of the lava moving faster than those beneath.

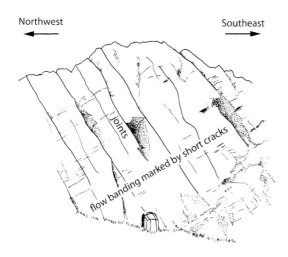

*Fig. **L20**. Flow-banding and joints in lava, Haystacks.*

We call this **flow-banding** and it tells us the orientation of the original ground surface, here tilted to the left (northwest) by later Earth movements. The joints and flow-banding make well-spaced natural steps for the climber. You will see more flow-banding higher up.

Herdwick sheep.

47

SCRATCHES ON A MOVEMENT SURFACE

Loc. **L21**, NY 192 133. As you climb the second crag the path crosses a large sloping slab 10 metres from top to bottom, which is covered with fine parallel grooves. These are slickensides, scratch marks formed when two fractured blocks of rock move relative to one another.

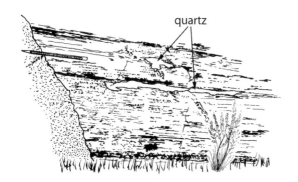

*Fig. **L21**. Slickensides. Unlike layers within a rock, the grooves are only on the surface where the movement occurred, and do not extend into the solid rock.*

The white **quartz** on some of the scratches was formed from hot groundwaters as the blocks moved. The grooves are parallel to the direction of movement. A second smaller grooved slab can be seen further up. We cannot tell when the movements took place, but it must have been after the lavas became fully solid.

Near the summit of Haystacks (NY 193 132) there is more flow-banding. Here it is noticeably wavy, due to irregular patterns of flow in the lava hereabouts – not to later folding, which would have affected the rock layers below as well.

The next Location is 1½ km ahead. Follow the path past Innominate Tarn to Blackbeck Tarn (NY 201 129), where it heads ENE to cross Warnscale Beck at NY 208 134. Ahead are the spoil heaps of the abandoned Dubs Quarry with a quarry building, now a climbers' hut, among them.

Innominate Tarn, resting place of Alfred Wainwright's ashes.

VALUABLE SLATES

Loc. **L22**, NY 211 134, Dubs Quarry. In Journal 2 we explained that cleavage is the effect of pressure on fine-grained rocks – whether they are sediments like those at Loc. **L6** or tuffs formed from volcanic ash. Where the cleavage is well-developed we call the rock a **slate**. All the slates used in the central Lake District for roofing and ornamental purposes come from cleaved tuffs. The tuffs we have described so far have been composed of particles of sand size or greater – too coarse for cleavage to be well-developed. Here at Dubs and in a zone stretching several kilometres to the northeast the tuffs are finer-grained and cleavage was able to develop strongly.

The best material has of course been removed, but there are plenty of good pickings on the spoil heaps. Choose a piece that shows stripes running across the smooth face. The stripes are bedding and the smooth face is cleavage.

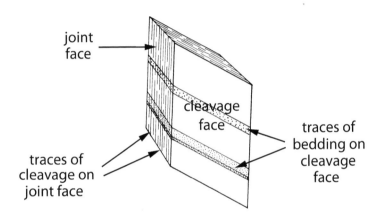

Fig. L22. An idealised block of slate showing how bedding, cleavage, and joints are related in three dimensions.

From the climbers' hut head east along the course of the old tramway. This rises gently to meet the alternative route from Ennerdale at NY 216 135 and thence descends with increasing steepness to Honister. The distance to the next Location is 1½ km.

A Coast-to-Coast coaster. Honister slate has many uses.

Loc. **L23**, NY 223 135, Yew Crag, Honister. As you walk down to the road, it's worth studying the hillside opposite as it shows bedding and cleavage on a large scale.

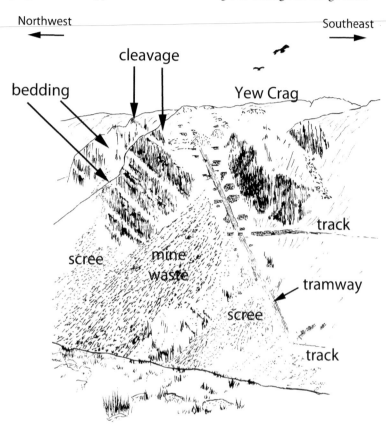

Fig. L23. View looking across the Honister Pass to the south end of Yew Crag.

The bedding in the tuffs shows as ledges dipping at 45° to the right. The cleavage appears as vertical cracks running through the exposures.

Loc. **L24**, NY 225 135, Honister Slate Works' car park. If you have time you might like to look around the exhibits that litter the car park; or even take a mine tour. The slates were so valuable that it was worth extracting them from underground, with all the extra expense involved – unusual, one might think, for mere building materials. But feel the quality!

The next Location is where a track to the left leaves the road, about 200 metres ahead.

MORE RESIDUE OF THE ICE AGE

Loc. **L25**, NY 228 137, at the join of the path and the road.

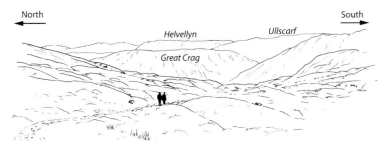

North   South

Helvellyn   Ullscarf

Great Crag

*Fig. **L25**. Little Gatesgarthdale.*

The bottom of Little Gatesgarthdale valley is covered by deposits of a glacier that flowed down it into Borrowdale. At the end of the Ice Age the glacier became stagnant. As it melted, the sediment that it carried – boulders, stones, sand, and clay – was dumped as irregular heaps of **moraine**, made of **boulder clay**. The material on the north side has been cut through by streams and so appears as lobes in contrast to the hummocks on the floor. See Journal **3** for more detail.

Continue on the track for another 2½ km. At Seatoller, Little Gatesgarthdale joins the broader valley of Seathwaite and the River Derwent. The very flat valley floor was formerly a lake 2½ km long, dammed further downstream by a glacial moraine which you will see at the next Location. Take the path along the north side of the main valley.

Loc. **L26**, NY 254 141, where the path crosses an ice-smoothed rock face on the north bank of the river. The south bank of the river is a good example of the cross-section of a **terminal moraine**, showing the unsorted mix of particle sizes from mud to large boulders.

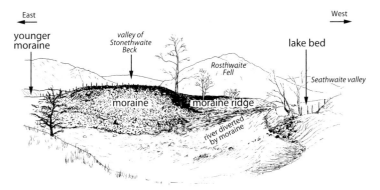

East   West

younger
moraine

valley of
Stonethwaite
Beck

lake bed

Rosthwaite
Fell

Seathwaite valley

moraine   moraine ridge

river diverted
by moraine

*Fig. **L26**. Moraine ridge with internal structure exposed.*

The moraine ridge dammed the lake on its upstream side and later presented a barrier to the present course of the river, which runs along its western side before breaking through at this Location. This moraine is one of several hereabouts – you can see a second in the distance on the left. We discuss them in Journal **3**.

Scramble carefully across the ice-smoothed rocks on the river bank (there is a fixed chain to assist) and continue along the path to Rosthwaite village.

JOURNAL 3 – ROSTHWAITE

HOW BIG, HOW MUCH, HOW FAST, HOW SLOW? (Loc. *L11*)

The nearly flat bed of the River Liza before it enters Ennerdale Water results from deposition of sediment eroded from the upper part of the valley since the end of the Ice Age, about 10,000 years ago. The rather simple geometry of the valley makes it possible to estimate the rates of some of the processes that have occurred in that span of time.

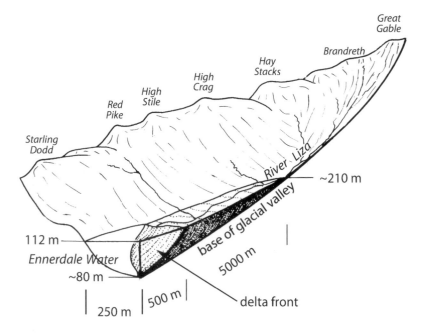

A dissection of the north half of upper Ennerdale. The sediments in the base of the valley were deposited as a delta, progressively leading to the present position of the delta front.

Using the dimensions in the drawing, and making simple assumptions about the shape of the valley (but sparing you the details of the calculation), we can estimate volumes and rates of processes:

- The total volume of the sediments is about 8 million cubic metres. This is about the same as the amount of rock eroded and then deposited within the area of upper Ennerdale in 10,000 years.

- So the average rates of erosion and deposition were about 800 cubic metres per year. (Locally they would have been much higher or lower than the average.)

- The area within the watershed of upper Ennerdale is about 27 square km, so an average of about 0.3 metres thickness has been eroded from the land surface in the 10,000 years.

- The average thickness of sediment deposited in the delta was about 0.6 mm per year.

- The rate of advance of the delta front at the present day is about 10 mm per year.

We can assume that before the Ice Age the valley was V-shaped. The Dartmoor Granite in Devon was not covered by ice, so the rivers there can be used as an indication of the possible shape of Ennerdale before the glaciation. Another piece of simple geometry leads to another useful estimate:

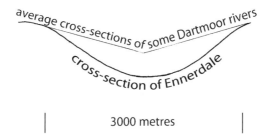

3000 metres

Cross-sections of valleys shaped by rivers and by a glacier.

- The area between the two cross-sections (about 0.75 square km) suggests a minimum estimate of the volume of rock in the Ennerdale valley that was eroded by the glacier. The whole length of Ennerdale is 12 km, so the amount of rock eroded was about 9 cubic km. This would be enough to cover much of the coastal area between the foot of Ennerdale and the coast at St Bees (say, 100 square km) with boulder clay to a depth of 50 to 100 metres.

By everyday standards, some of the numbers are very large (8 million cubic metres – perhaps a million lorryloads!) and some are very small (0.6 millimetres per year – imperceptible!). Though they are all based on "back-of-the-envelope" calculations, they do give an idea of the rates of some of the natural processes going on all around us. It is a characteristic of many geological processes that one must deal with very large and very small numbers. A consequence is that very slow processes continued for very long spans of time can produce very large effects.

You could entertain yourself by thinking through the assumptions we have made in producing these estimates, and finding the errors and omissions. (An example: how does the amount of eroded rock held in screes affect the results?)

TWO-STAGE COOLING OF MAGMA (Loc. *L17*)

See the drawing on page 55.

Magmas are formed at depth and rise through the crust, cooling as they do so. If the magma rises rapidly to the surface in one movement it solidifies as a lava made of small crystals, as shown in the upper drawing on the next page. But if the rise is interrupted so that the magma stops for a while below the surface as shown in the lower drawing it can cool enough for some crystals to form, even though the rest of the magma is still liquid. Renewed upward movement (either to the surface as a lava or to near the surface as an intrusion) allows the rest of the liquid to cool rapidly, producing small crystals. The result is a rock with two crystal sizes – larger ones formed at depth and smaller ones formed at or near the surface.

ASH FLOWS AND WELDED TUFFS (Loc. *L18*)

Violent eruptions produce columns of hot gas and blobs of liquid magma, reaching heights of 10 km or more into the atmosphere. When such a column collapses, or when an eruption emerges from a side-vent, a dense cloud of very hot gas and magma flows down the flanks of the volcano (see Journal **2**, Volcanic Rocks, Drawing c). If the blobs of magma are still partly liquid when the flow comes to rest, they solidify in place to produce what is called a **welded tuff**. Individual tuffs can be many tens of metres thick. Ash-flow eruptions are really impressive, as at Mount Pinatubo in 1991. They are also very dangerous, because the flows can be very large, travelling at great speed, and their interiors are searingly hot.

If the blobs of magma are still plastic when the flow stops moving, the weight of the flow squashes them vertically, so they get flattened horizontally. Although the rock has no layering as such, the parallel orientation of the blobs gives it a structure like a box of squashed tomatoes. The present-day tilt, or **dip**, of the flattened blobs can be used to tell us if the rock has been tilted since it was deposited, as in Fig. **L18**.

The rock at Loc. **L18** also contains unsquashed fragments. When these were erupted they were solid, perhaps torn off the sides of the vent. So they retained their shapes while the semi-liquid ones were squashed.

As we walk on from Rosthwaite to Patterdale we shall find that tuffs, of all kinds, become by far the predominant kind of volcanic rock. This marks a very significant change in the style of volcanism in the history of the Lake District, which we shall explain in detail in Journal **4**.

TWO POSSIBLE PATTERNS OF
SOLIDIFICATION OF A MAGMA

Rapid rise

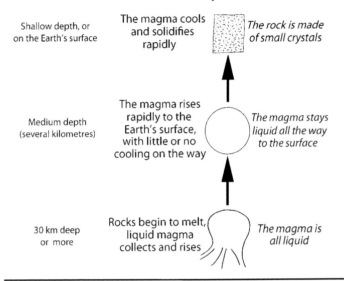

Shallow depth, or on the Earth's surface — The magma cools and solidifies rapidly — *The rock is made of small crystals*

Medium depth (several kilometres) — The magma rises rapidly to the Earth's surface, with little or no cooling on the way — *The magma stays liquid all the way to the surface*

30 km deep or more — Rocks begin to melt, liquid magma collects and rises — *The magma is all liquid*

Interrupted rise

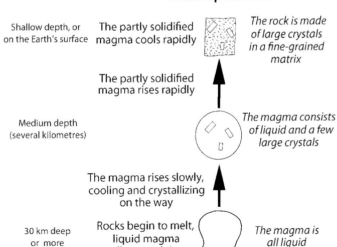

Shallow depth, or on the Earth's surface — The partly solidified magma cools rapidly — *The rock is made of large crystals in a fine-grained matrix*

The partly solidified magma rises rapidly

Medium depth (several kilometres) — *The magma consists of liquid and a few large crystals*

The magma rises slowly, cooling and crystallizing on the way

30 km deep or more — Rocks begin to melt, liquid magma collects and rises — *The magma is all liquid*

CRAG-AND-LEDGE SCENERY AND ANCIENT LAND SURFACES (Loc. *L19*)

On Haystacks (Loc. **L19**) we saw how the fellside was composed of alternating steep crags and more gently sloping ledges. Fig. **L19/2** shows how this relates to the underlying structure. The contacts between successive lava flows are relatively easily weathered for three reasons. First, lava eruptions are often accompanied by minor eruptions of ash. This rains down on the lava surface forming a layer of relatively easily weathered tuff. Second, where there is a significant time gap between eruption of successive lavas, weathering will have taken place at the time of eruption – i.e. during the Ordovician. As you walk over one of the ledges on Haystacks you are in a sense walking on a 450-million-year-old land surface. A third reason is that the contact is a physical break, along which modern groundwaters can readily percolate and so cause enhanced weathering. On Haystacks the boundaries are obscured by the present-day soil and loose rock debris.

We shall see lots more examples of crag-and-ledge scenery during the Walk, and not only in volcanic rocks.

FEATURES OF THE ICE AGE IN BORROWDALE (Loc. *L26*)

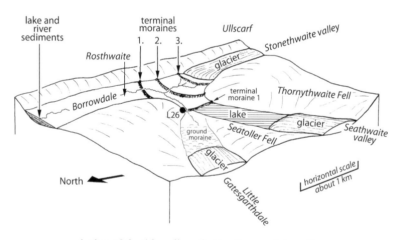

A view of the side valleys of upper Borrowdale as they might have been towards the end of the Ice Age.

During the Ice Age all the valleys you can see from Rosthwaite contained glaciers. The last glacier to melt occupied the valley of what is now Stonethwaite Beck. At three stages of its retreat, starting 18,000 years ago, the forward flow of the ice (and the rocky debris within it) kept pace with the rate of melting. The resulting ridges of debris, called **terminal moraines**, were deposited at the glacier front. The drawing shows their positions, with No. 3 the last to be formed.

The oldest moraine, No. 1, formed a dam holding back a temporary lake in the Seathwaite valley. It was later broken through by the river at Loc. **L26**, and the moraine is still a barrier to the present-day course of the river.

THE WALK – ROSTHWAITE TO PATTERDALE

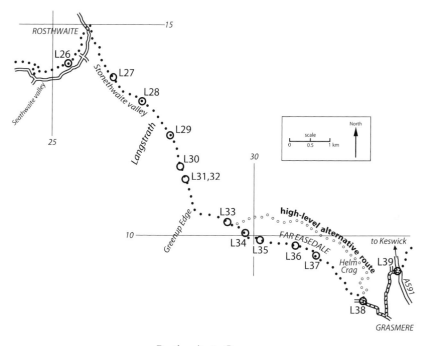

Rosthwaite to Grasmere.

From Rosthwaite follow the Keswick road for 50 metres, turn right down a lane leading to Hazel Bank, cross the bridge over Stonethwaite Beck, and follow the path upstream on the east side to the next Location, 1½ km from Rosthwaite.

MORE WELDED TUFFS

Loc. **L27**, NY 265 138. As you approach Galleny Force, the view ahead is dominated by Eagle Crag. Like the lavas on Haystacks (Fig. **L19/2**), the rocks on Eagle Crag form several tiers of steep crags. However, on Eagle Crag the rocks are not lavas but **welded tuffs**. Both rocks are formed from material that flows down the slope of a volcano as a coherent mass, and so both rocks form erosion-resistant crags. By contrast the bedrocks of Greenup Edge, in the background, are **ash-fall** deposits or unwelded tuffs, made from a rain of individual grains. This makes them less resistant to erosion and they form gentle slopes.

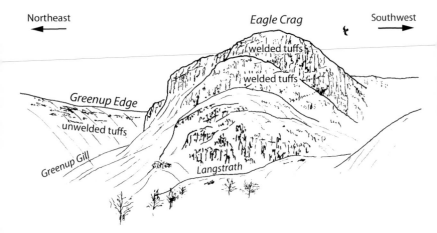

Northeast ← *Eagle Crag* Southwest →

welded tuffs

welded tuffs

Greenup Edge

unwelded tuffs

Greenup Gill

Langstrath

Fig. L27. Eagle Crag from Galleny Force.

Continue along the path for 1 km.

Loc. **L28**, NY 272 132. Above Galleny Force on the right of the path are four stout *hecks* – horizontally hung gates where a beck flows across the path and through the wall. Note the abundant red-weathering pebbles in the beck. If the sun is shining you may see small crystals in them that flash in the light. These rocks probably come from lavas on the slopes above, though they could equally well be sills; as we have said before, the two are hard to distinguish. The red colour derives from a relatively high content of iron, something that varies considerably in igneous rocks.

Walk on for another 1 km to a gate across the path.

GLACIERS AND RIVERS: CONTRASTING EROSION STYLES

Loc. **L29**, NY 279 123. Pause here to see how the cross-profile of the valley changes as you go up. Downstream, beyond Galleny Force, the profile is broad and flat-bottomed – typical of a glacier-carved valley partially filled by lake sediment. Upstream it is V-shaped – characteristic of erosion by water. At the height of the Ice Age the valley was filled by a glacier. Later, as the climate warmed, the glacier melted and its front receded to the head of the valley – above where you are now. As the large quantity of water generated by the melting flowed steeply down it eroded the upper parts of the valley, producing the V-shaped profile. The eroded material was deposited on the more gently sloping floor of the lower valley, partly filling it in. We shall see evidence for the valley-head glacier shortly.

Stay on the path for another ½ km to Lining Crag.

As you walk on, look at the pebbles in the path; you should see rough-surfaced rocks (coarse tuff), layered rocks (bedded tuff), and streaky rocks (welded tuff). The variety of rock-types indicates the wide range of processes that went on in the making of the Lake District volcanoes.

Loose stones and boulders on footpaths in northern England are not necessarily clues to the surrounding bedrock – they may have been moved by glaciers or indeed by humans. However, we are here close to the centre of the Lake District mountains, which forms a watershed. Any rocks that we see will have come from between here and this watershed, whether they were carried by streams or glaciers. The exception of course is material helicoptered in to make footpaths – but there is no evidence of this from here up.

MORE TUFFS

Loc. **L30**, NY 282 117. The charming cove beneath Lining Crag is the site of the valley-head glacier that we mentioned under Loc. **L29**. The hummocks that litter its floor are moraines; their large size shows that the glacier occupied the cove for a substantial period of time.

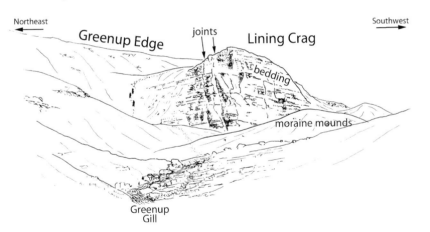

*Fig. **L30**. Lining Crag from Greenup Gill, showing bedding and joints.*

At first sight Lining Crag may appear featureless. However, in reasonable lighting one can pick out two sets of cracks: one nearly vertical and one tilted at low angles to the left and right of the crag. The vertical ones are randomly spaced and cannot be followed for any great distance – these are joints. By contrast, the gently inclined cracks are more continuous and strikingly parallel. In places they are marked by grass-covered ledges. They mark bedding planes in the tuffs.

Follow the path towards the foot of Lining Crag and stop about 70 metres short of it, at a metre-long boulder of bedded tuff on level ground to the right of the path.

59

Loc. **L31**, NY 283 114. The boulder contains structures that reveal an aspect of how volcanoes develop.

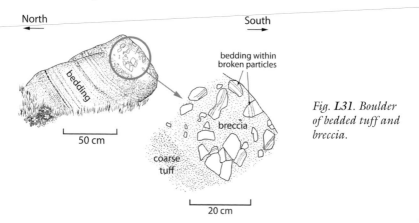

*Fig. **L31**. Boulder of bedded tuff and breccia.*

The breccia contains fist-sized chunks, which themselves have internal bedding. These chunks are fragments of a continuous layer of bedded tuff that was deposited earlier on the flanks of the volcano. Chunks of the layer were picked up by streams, transported, and re-deposited further downslope. The bedded tuff must have been compact enough for sizeable fragments to survive the transport without breaking up. So there was time for compaction between original deposition of the bed and its subsequent erosion – probably months and possibly years.

Continue to the foot of Lining Crag.

At the foot of the crag, next to the path are clues to the gently inclined structures that we saw from a distance (Loc. **L30**). Through the lichen you can see fine stripes of different shades of grey running across the face. The stripes are continuous, so they are bedding. Like the bedding on High Stile summit (Loc. **L15**), some of the layers cut across others, indicating transport by flowing water. So the rocks are **reworked tuffs**. Following the bedding round corners in the rock shows that it is dipping, at a gentle angle, towards the southeast – *into the cliff*. This explains the impression we had from a distance, where the banding appeared to dip to right and left.

The path climbs steeply left of Lining Crag and continues upwards to the SSE for ¾ km across a boggy expanse underlain by peat.

Loc. **L32**, NY 285 105. Greenup Edge, the pass between Greenup Gill and Wyth Burn. On the approach to the pass the Route crosses numerous exposures of tuff, much of it coarse and some of it bedded. Significantly, there are places where you can see squashed particles like those at Loc. **L18** – evidence of ash flows. Where bedding is visible it is nearly horizontal; so these rocks must overlie the reworked tuffs that we passed on Lining Crag, lower down.

From Greenup Edge the Route heads downhill to the east. Where the path splits keep to the right. (Don't take the path to the left, which will lead you into Wainwright's "Wythburn Trap" – a detour that takes you far to the north of the Route.) Descend ¾ km, across ground that slopes down to your left, to the level bottom at Birks – the lowest point of this section of the path. On a fine day this remote spot can be a sheltered sun-trap. In case you decide to stop and do some detective work we've included some geological puzzles for you at the next locality. They will reveal more about how volcanic ash is deposited, so it's worth spending a little time here.

A PUZZLE OF LAYERS

Loc. **L33**, NY 294 103. Some 30 metres before you reach Birks Gill, the lowest point of the path, there are a few large boulders of bedded tuff close to the path. We've chosen the largest to study. It will involve looking closely at the fine detail in the rock.

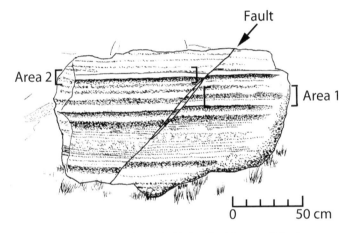

Fig. L33/1. Boulder of bedded tuff with a small fault.

The first thing to notice about the boulder is that the continuity of the layers is displaced by a feature called a **fault** – in effect a fracture combined with relative movement along the break. Rocks can be deformed in a variety of ways, and faults are one of the commonest styles of deformation. Though the fault in this boulder is very small it has many features just like much larger faults, so it's worth looking at carefully. We explain faults in more detail in Journal **4**.

Next, let's see what the layers of the rock are like. Feeling the rock surface with a fingertip reveals that different layers have different grain sizes. The finer layers are paler than the coarser ones. This is a common feature in tuffs. (In mudstones the colour contrast is the other way round, as we saw at Loc. **L3**.) Some of the boundaries between layers are sharp, but in other places the layers grade into each other. Apart from the effect of the fault, most of the boundaries are straight – or planar in three dimensions. A few are not; we'll return to these, and to the fault, shortly.

61

Now for a bit of interpretation. We'll put it in the form of puzzles. We consider possible answers in the Journal.

Puzzle 1. Was the ash deposited on land or under water?

The clues to this lie in the detail of the layering. Here are some features which suggest formation under water. See if you can find examples in the boulder. (*Hint: look in the labelled areas in Fig. L33/1.*)

a) Scours

Streams are common on volcanoes. If they are strong enough they can scour out channels in loose ash. Further deposition fills in the irregularities in the eroded surface (Fig. **L33/2**). See if you can find examples in the boulder.

b) Ripples

Waves, in lakes or in the sea, can form ripples in any sand-size material: sediment or ash.

When things calm down, mud or fine ash that was in suspension in the water settles out, draping over the ripple surfaces. Further deposition fills in the hollows and drapes over the crests (Fig. **L33/3**). See if you can find examples in the boulder.

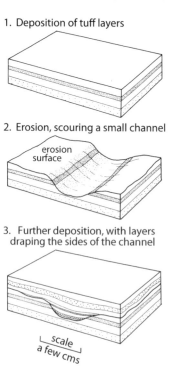

1. Deposition of tuff layers

2. Erosion, scouring a small channel

   erosion surface

3. Further deposition, with layers draping the sides of the channel

   scale
   a few cms

Fig. L33/2. How a scour forms and fills.

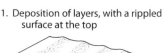

1. Deposition of layers, with a rippled surface at the top

2. Deposition of mud, draping over the rippled surface

3. Deposition of further layers, draping over the ripples

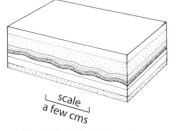

   scale
   a few cms

Fig. L33/3. Ripples and how they get buried.

Puzzle 2. How can we tell whether the layers are right-way up; i.e. the boulder has not been turned over during transport? (*Hint: is the interpretation of Figs L33/2 and L33/3 the same if turned upside down?*)

Puzzle 3. How can we tell how long it took the layers in the boulder to be deposited (hours, days, months, thousands of years)?

This is a meaningful question – the answer would tell us how quickly the volcano grew – but it's not easy to determine. One clue is compaction. When they are first deposited, grains of ash or sediment are separate, like the loose sand in a dune at the back of a beach. With time they settle down and a firm compaction surface forms on top, as on beach sand after the tide has gone out. This surface will appear as a well-defined change in the sequence of the layers. A second clue is the different effects of scouring on loose and on compacted ash. (*Hint: look at the labelled areas in Fig. L33/1.*)

Puzzle 4. What is peculiar about the fault?

The first two things that you probably notice are: (i) the block to the left has moved downwards relative to the one on the right; (ii) the fault splits for part of its length, with a sliver in the middle that has moved down about half as much as the left block. You will find these effects in many faults. The feature that needs explaining is the *amount of movement* along the fault. Choose two beds that you can trace across the fault – one near the top and one near the bottom. How much have the beds moved relative to each other? Is it the same for both beds? What about the beds in between? Can you explain any differences? (*Hint: think about how the time when the fault moved might relate to the time when the ash was being deposited.*)

Puzzle 5. Given that this boulder and those around it have been transported by ice, why are they not more rounded?

The Route continues eastwards across Birks Gill over boggy ground and up to the (unnamed) pass that leads down Far Easedale to Grasmere, marked by two metal posts.

A WATERSHED

The pass at the head of Far Easedale is a significant watershed. Rain falling west of it drains northward into Thirlmere and thence into the Irish Sea. Rainfall to the east drains into Windermere and Morecambe Bay to the south.

From the pass we shall take the valley route down Far Easedale; if you follow Wainwright's high-level alternative along the ridge to the north you will be able to see many of the features that we describe, in the valley below on your right. The next location is in about ½ km.

Descend eastward over gradually steepening ground. The crags of Broadstone Head appear on the right, and beyond them Ferngill Crag, curving round to form the southern edge of the semicircular hollow of Moor Moss.

A VALLEY WITH STEPS

Loc. **L34**, NY 299 101, Moor Moss. This is the first of three glacially eroded hollows that form steps in the long profile of Far Easedale. The lip of each of these hollows is a resistant band of rock that crosses the valley – the one here is clearly visible in the contours on the 1:25,000 OS map, running down from the northeast.

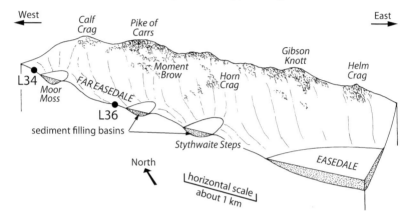

*Fig. **L34**. Cartoon of Far Easedale showing the stepped profile and the sediment-filled basins.*

As the glacier that occupied Far Easedale receded, the hollows became filled with glacial sediment washed out of the glacier by meltwater streams, giving them flattish floors. Rapid melting of the stagnant remains of the glacier left hummocky moraines – now covered with bracken – like the ones at Loc. **L25**.

As the path steepens below Moor Moss, more of the Far Easedale valley with its characteristic U-shaped glacier-cut cross-profile becomes visible.

Loc. **L35**, NY 301 099. On the right is Deer Bields, an imposing cliff which rises up from the valley floor in a series of tilted ledges, each capping a small crag. We saw a similar feature on Haystacks (Fig. **L19/2**), where the ledges are the tops of lava flows. Here they are the tops of tuff beds, and Deer Bields and the slopes below are made of a stack of these. Good lighting will reveal that the ledges slope down to the left – showing that the beds have been tilted eastward.

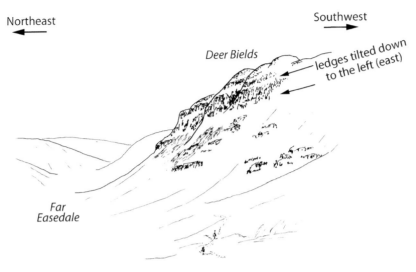

Northeast ◄

Southwest ►

Deer Bields

ledges tilted down to the left (east)

Far Easedale

Fig. **L35**. *Deer Bields from Moor Moss showing crag-and-ledge structure.*

Continue down the path for about 1 km.

BOULDER CLAY AGAIN

Loc. **L36**, NY 310 098. Ahead you can see a second, larger flat-floored infilled hollow in the valley floor with bracken-covered moraine mounds around it. The Route passes through these and in places footpath erosion has revealed their interior – an unsorted mixture of clay, silt, sand, gravel, pebbles, and boulders left by the glacier as it melted. This is **boulder clay** – the first we have seen for a long time, even though it covers much of the lower ground of the Walk like a blanket.

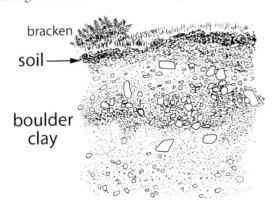

bracken

soil →

boulder clay

Fig. L36. Boulder clay. Note the random arrangement of pebbles and boulders, lack of layering, and the dark organic-rich soil on top.

65

The clay content has meant that quite a thick soil has developed, and this has supported the growth of bracken – toxic to livestock and labour-intensive to eradicate. With the progressive reduction in farm labour forces, this highly adaptable plant has colonised many of the hillsides in the Grasmere district, including the walled-in pastures on the lower slopes.

Below Moment Brow the valley narrows at the second step in its long profile and the path descends more steeply over boulder-strewn slopes – the remnants of moraines from which the finer particles have been washed by water. The next Location is ½ km ahead.

MORE BRECCIA

Loc. **L37**, NY 315 096. Here the Route rejoins Far Easedale Gill. Beside the path some 30 metres upstream of a tree-filled section of the gill are rough-surfaced rounded exposures. The rocks are unlayered and have numerous recesses up to around 10 cm across.

10 cm

Fig. L37. Volcanic breccia with internally layered fragments.

The rock is a breccia and the recesses are large volcanic fragments which have weathered more rapidly than the tuff matrix – like the welded tuffs at Loc. **L18**. The layering in some of the large particles shows that they have had a two-stage history, as at Loc. **L31**.

Follow the path until you are opposite a sheepfold on the flattish valley floor (NY 315 095) – this is the third infilled hollow.

Above to the north is Horn Crag and the features on the slopes on its east side are crag-and-ledge structures, like those on Deer Bields (Loc. L35) and, like them, sloping down valley.

COMBINED GLACIERS, MORE EROSION

Continue down the path for 2 km, crossing the main gill by a footbridge at Stythwaite Steps (NY 318 094), which marks the lip of the third infilled hollow, and descending among exposures of unlayered coarse tuff to the lower valley.

Here the combined erosive power of the glacier in Far Easedale and a glacier coming in from Sour Milk Gill to the south has eroded a broader and deeper basin. As the glaciers receded, meltwater deposited sediment on the valley floor to form the flattish land east of Brimmer Head Farm.

Where the path leaves the woods and becomes a tarmac road, it is worth pausing to take in the views.

Loc. **L38**, NY 327 084. To the west towards Easedale one can see more crag-and-ledge scenery, here indicating that the volcanic strata dip to the north.

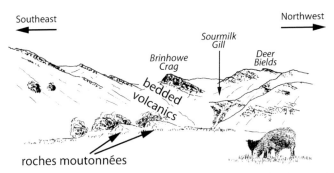

Fig. L38/1. View towards Easedale showing terracing dipping north.

Closer are two humps of bedrock, their surfaces smoothed by rock fragments embedded in the base of the glacier. The humps are asymmetrical: the left-hand down-glacier sides are steeper than the up-glacier sides on the right. These are roches moutonnées.

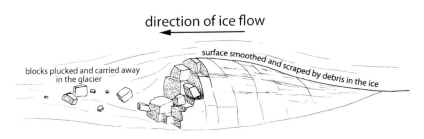

Fig. L38/2. How a roche moutonnée forms.

67

Roches moutonnées form where ice flows over irregularities in bedrock. The weight of a glacier is sufficient to cause melting at its base. This lubricates the flow, as happens in ice-skating. The water percolates into cracks in the bedrock, where the pressure is relatively lower, and freezes. The freezing causes expansion, breaking off blocks of bedrock which become entrained in the flowing ice – a process known as plucking.

To the north is the imposing triangle of Helm Crag, which we'll describe from the far side where its structure is clearer.

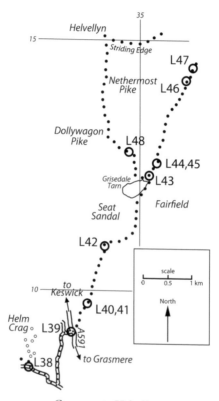

Grasmere to Helvellyn.

At Grasmere the Walk crosses the broad north-south trending valley of the River Rothay, which follows a major fracture, the Coniston Fault. This fault runs southward from Threlkeld in the north to Coniston Water and beyond. The next Location is 1½ km from Loc. **L38**. You could either turn left at Goody Bridge into the side road to Mill Bridge or walk on into Grasmere and then north on the A591 road.

SILLS AND CLEAVED TUFFS

Loc. **L39**, NY 336 092. Mill Bridge. From here we get another view of Helm Crag.

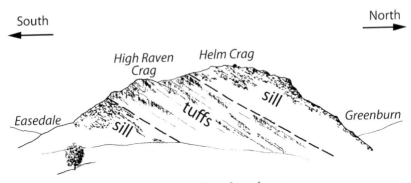

*Fig. **L39**. Helm Crag from the east.*

The poorly exposed rocks in the central part of the view are **bedded tuffs**, dipping to the north, and with clearly visible vertical cleavage. Above and below are **sills**, intruded as liquid magma parallel with the layering of the tuffs, and now forming steep crags like those on Fleetwith Pike (Fig. **L16**).

The sills belong to a set that extends south as far as Great Langdale. When the magmas that formed them were intruded, the land surface was considerably higher than now. The magmas failed to reach the surface and solidified in cracks in the older volcanic rocks that make up the lower parts of the volcano, becoming part of the volcano's plumbing.

From Mill Bridge take the bridleway to the northeast. To the right is the gorge carved in the steep sides of the Grasmere valley by the glacier-fed ancestor of Tongue Gill. In and beside the path are occasional small exposures of cleaved tuff with distinctive parallel cracks where the cleavage crosses the weathered surface. Walk up for ¾ km to a footbridge across Tongue Gill, but stop 75 metres before you reach the bridge.

MORE TUFFS, BRECCIA, AND A LOBE OF MORAINE

Loc. **L40**, NY 339 097, where the path crosses a large exposure of tuff. The exposure has cleavage cracks and a stepped surface. The top of each step represents the top of a bed – a miniature version of the crag-and-ledge structure seen at Loc. **L35**.

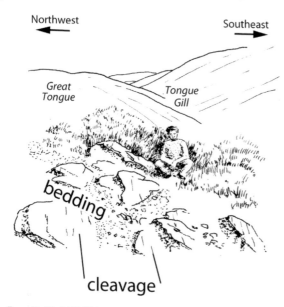

Northwest ←   Southeast →

Great Tongue

Tongue Gill

bedding

cleavage

Fig. L40. Tuff exposure in the path.

Loc. **L41**, NY 339 098. At the footbridge and adjacent ford, Tongue Gill is joined from the north by Little Tongue Gill. Between them rears the mass of Great Tongue, which we explain at the next Location, where we see it from the top end.

From the footbridge follow the track beside Little Tongue Gill (on the left) for 1 km. Here a diversion through bracken takes you to the base of Hause Riggs crag.

Loc. **L42**, NY 343 109. Hause Riggs crag contains much coarser deposits than those at Loc. **L40**. In some places the particles are up to fist-size, set in a finer matrix of tuff, so this is a breccia. The lack of cleavage and wide spacing of joints explain why these rocks form a prominent crag.

Skirt the left side of Hause Riggs to the top of the crag and follow the path eastwards for around 200 metres.

From here there is a fine view of Great Tongue and the fells beyond, from Coniston Old Man in the south to Bowfell in the north.

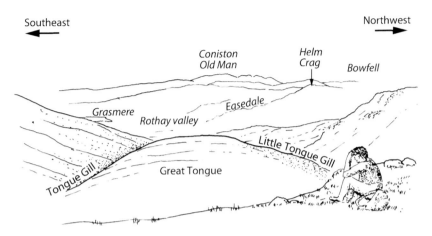

Fig. I42. Great Tongue from above showing how it forms a lobe pointing down valley.

Great Tongue's rounded shape, the lack of bedrock exposure, and the abundance of boulders on it suggest that it is a moraine, not bedrock. The lobe shape implies that it may have moved downslope since it was deposited. We discuss this in Journal **4**.

It is 2 km to the next Location. Follow the path northeastwards for 400 metres to its junction with the path up from Tongue Gill at NY 349 112. From here the path climbs for ½ km to Hause Gap.

Much of this path has been re-laid. Most of the blocks are tuffs of various grain-sizes, and the passage of feet has kept them lichen-free. Their colours range from heavily weathered pale straw to lightly weathered greenish blue-grey. Many of the rocks used by the path builders were brought in by helicopter, so they have probably come from elsewhere.

Descend to the outlet of Grisedale Tarn. From here Wainwright describes two alternative routes: a low-level one down Grisedale and a high-level one over Helvellyn and Striding Edge. The low-level Route (to be described first) gives more insights into how volcanoes work; the high-level Route includes some of the finest post-glacial scenery in the country.

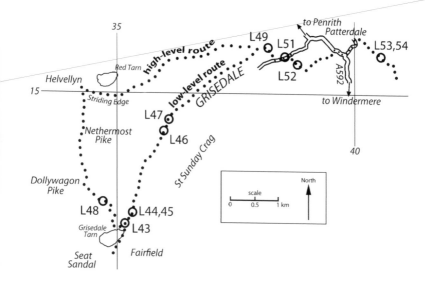

Grisedale Tarn to Patterdale.

GRISEDALE TARN TO PATTERDALE: THE LOW-LEVEL ROUTE

A LAVA, AND AN INTRIGUING CONTACT BETWEEN TWO TUFFS

Loc. **L43**, NY 352 123. To the right of the path and about 50 metres downstream from the tarn's outlet are some small waterfalls. A few metres north of the highest one are rocks with a distinctive knobbly appearance. The knobbles are blocks from 2 to 15 cm across, with finer material between. You are looking at the top of a lava flow.

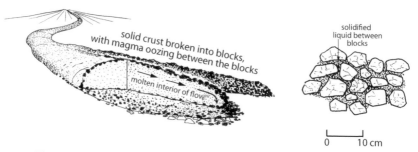

Fig. L43. A blocky lava flow. The nearest part shows the movement of the interior. The detail on the right shows autobrecciation in the resulting lava.

As a lava flows forwards its top surface cools, causing it to crust over. Continued movement breaks the crust into blocks and as these are carried along they jostle one other, rounding their corners. Meanwhile magma from below seeps up through the gaps and solidifies, forming the finer material between the blocks. This process is called autobrecciation – the movement of the lava caused its surface to break up into a breccia.

This Location provides a view of the upper part of Grisedale with a glimpse of Ullswater and the lowlands of the Eden Valley beyond. You will see more of this view from Loc. **L48**.

Follow the path that leads northeast towards Grisedale for 250 metres.

Loc. **L44**, NY 353 125. The path crosses two screes, which provide convenient samples of the rocks in Tarn Crag above. The first scree is a very coarse tuff with particles up to 5 cm across. The second is fine-grained, and composed of crystals which twinkle in sunlight. Some of the crystals are visible with the unaided eye, so the rock is a lava or sill formed by two-stage cooling, as explained in Journal **3**.

Continue 50 metres down the path from the second scree.

Loc. **L45**, NY 354 126. Here the path crosses extensive exposures of coarse tuff, mostly unbedded. Have a look at the northern (left-hand) edge of these exposures.

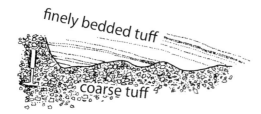

Fig. L45. An ash flow (coarse tuff) covered by fine ash (finely bedded tuff).

In places you should see patches of tuff with thin bedding. The contact between the two tuffs, bedded and unbedded, is interesting. The upper surface of the coarse tuff is irregular and the bedded tuff fills in the hollows in the surface, rather like fine sugar sifted (very generously) over the rough surface of a fruit crumble. Probably the coarse tuff (the crumble) was deposited from an ash flow sweeping down the volcano slopes, and the bedded tuff (the sugar) settled on its surface from the cloud of fine ash above the ash flow. In this case there was enough fine ash to completely cover the coarse tuff.

The next Location is 2 km ahead. Continue on the path, and after 1 km the narrow valley of Ruthwaite Beck appears on the left. This drains Ruthwaite Cove, one of three corries that were carved by tributaries of the main Grisedale glacier. From Ruthwaite Lodge climbing hut (NY 355 135) the path follows the beck downhill and in 250 metres the route divides. We shall follow the path on the north side of Grisedale. Note though that the bridleway on the south side is the faster route.

Loc. **L46**, NY 359 142, where the path crosses a line of gashes running down from Eagle Crag.

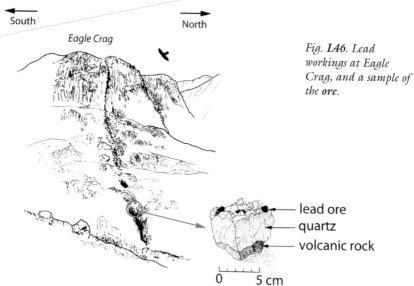

South ← North →

Eagle Crag

*Fig. L46. Lead workings at Eagle Crag, and a sample of the **ore**.*

— lead ore
— quartz
— volcanic rock

0   5 cm

The mines worked **veins** that cross the valley roughly E-W. On Eagle Crag the line of the vein is picked out by surface excavations producing the scar that runs up the hillside. There was a total of nine levels, one above the other. The vein had been worked for hundreds of years, but ceased to be profitable by 1880. As is the case with all old mine workings, entering them is potentially dangerous. If you are lucky you may find minerals in spoil heaps, although these will already have been picked over by mineral hunters.

The main **ore** mineral was the lead sulphide galena, with minor quantities of copper and antimony minerals. Here, and at the (much larger) Greenside Mine 3 km north, the metals plus much dissolved silica were carried by hot groundwaters circulating through cracks in the volcanic rocks. As the rising waters reached higher, cooler rocks they deposited their dissolved load as veins of quartz and ore mineral, filling the cracks.

Continue down the path for 300 metres.

Loc. **L47**, NY 361 144. Footbridge over Nethermostcove Beck. On the other side of Grisedale a small spoil heap marks another working. This is probably in an eastward continuation of the Eagle Crag vein. To judge by the size of the spoil heap this venture was much less productive, perhaps because the vein was thinner or the proportion of ore less.

The view across the valley is dominated by the steep cliffs of St Sunday Crag, crossed by horizontal lines which are bedding. The main rock you see from here is comparatively pale. Though we don't expect you to climb up to verify this, it is a tuff that has been reworked by water, which has given it the prominent bedding.

The path drops down towards the wall that marks the northern edge of the enclosed land on the valley floor. From there it roughly follows the contour for 2 km to Loc. L49, which we describe at the end of the next section.

GRISEDALE TARN TO PATTERDALE: THE HIGH-LEVEL ROUTE

From the tarn the route zig-zags northwestward up the side of Dollywaggon Pike. There are no exposures, but the boulders used to make the path sample a range of local rocks, again kept lichen-free by the passage of feet. Studying a few may relieve the tedium of the climb. The rocks include coarse tuff, bedded tuff, some welded tuff, and a fine-grained crystalline rock which probably came from a sill.

GLACIAL EROSION: CORRIES AND VALLEYS

Loc. **L48**, NY 348 128. Where the path levels off near the summit of Dollywaggon Pike there is a fine view down Grisedale to Place Fell, Ullswater, and, in clear weather, the Eden Valley beyond. In the foreground is Cock Cove, one of three east-facing **corries** carved by glaciers that sourced the larger glacier in Grisedale.

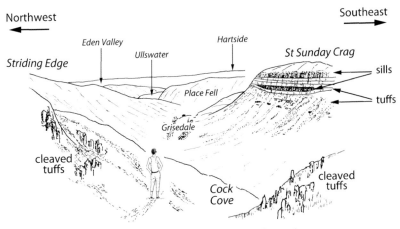

Fig. L48/1. View of Grisedale from the southeast shoulder of Dollywaggon Pike.

The greater erosive power of the Grisedale glacier cut a deeper valley so that Cock Cove, Nethermost Cove, and Ruthwaite Cove are now perched above it as hanging valleys.

The rocks in Cock Cove are cleaved tuffs, and the slabby appearance of the crags on its north and south sides is due to the **cleavage**. Its strike direction is NE-SW – the same as we saw at Nannycatch, Honister, and Easedale, and will see again beyond

75

Patterdale. This persistent direction shows that the stresses producing the cleavage were constant over a very wide area – an indication of the huge geographical scale of the processes operating on this region of the crust. We explain this in Journal **5**.

As you walk up to Dollywaggon Pike summit you can see cleavage in the rocks exposed in the path. The cleavage runs across the ridge in a constant direction, but in places its dip appears to vary. This is due to slow downslope movement of the loose surface material in which the cleaved rocks are embedded – a phenomenon known as soil creep. The uppermost parts of the soil move faster than those below, so that the cleavage is gradually rotated.

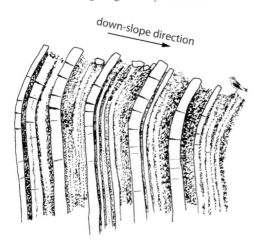

Fig. L48/2. Bending of cleavage by soil creep downslope.

Continue north along the broad ridge to the summit of Helvellyn – 2½ km from the last Location. There's a fine view of St Sunday Crag from above Ruthwaite Cove. The slabby rocks underfoot are tuffs split along the cleavage by frost action. Where bedrock is exposed the cleavage trends uniformly NE-SW.

Before leaving Helvellyn it's worth noting the contrast between its east- and west-facing slopes. To the east the slopes are gouged into steep-sided glacially eroded corries; to the west they descend evenly to the north-trending valley of Thirlmere. We discuss this in Journal **4**.

The next Location is 4 km ahead. In fine weather the views are magnificent; if the visibility is poor you will need maximum attention for keeping to the Route. From the shelter on Helvellyn summit take the well-worn path ESE; it soon steepens into a scramble down to the narrow ridge of Striding Edge. Though not as sharp as arêtes in the Alps, some of which the climber can sit astride with a foot in each valley, it's the best example that the Lake District affords.

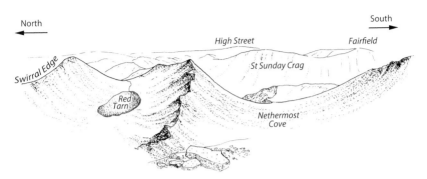

*The arête of Striding Edge (centre), viewed from Helvellyn,
flanked by the corries of Nethermost Cove and Red Tarn.*

During the traverse of Striding Edge most walkers will be content to concentrate on where to place hands and feet. In fact the only obvious rock structures for the first kilometre or so are cleavage and joints – which provide the hand- and foot-holds on the steep sections.

Loc. **L49**, NY 353 151. East of High Spying How the path broadens and drops a little to the north side of the ridge. Here the eagle-eyed may notice pale-coloured well-bedded rocks (reworked tuffs) which form uncleaved blocks on the path. These have slid down from the exposures on the ridge crest above. They are the same rock unit as the reworked tuffs that we saw at a distance on St Sunday Crag.

Follow the path down the broad northeast ridge to a prominent wall, where it meets a path that ascends from Red Tarn at Hole-in-the-Wall (NY 359 155). Cross the wall and follow the path diagonally downward into Grisedale for a little over 2 km. Avoid the path on the north side of the wall, which leads to Glenridding. Just below a small wood, Brownend Plantation, the high-level route joins the low-level one.

Loc. **L50**, NY 382 159. Brownend Plantation. From here there is a fine view of the south side of Grisedale.

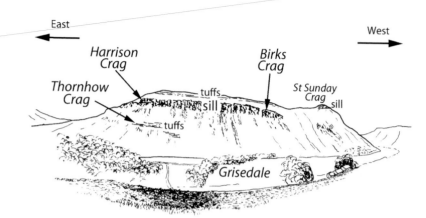

*Fig. **L50**. The view south from Brownend Plantation, showing pale-weathering reworked tuffs, intruded by a sill.*

At the top are pale rocks with a horizontal structure forming low crags with relatively fine scree at their base. Below are dark brownish-grey rocks that form the steep cliffs of Harrison and Birks Crags. The lowest rocks visible, on Thornhow Crag and the crags to its right, are again pale grey with a horizontal structure. The joints here are widely spaced and this has caused the blocks in the scree below to be larger than those in the screes at the top, where joints are more frequent.

The pale rocks on the skyline and on Thornhow Crag are the same reworked tuffs that we saw on St Sunday Crag; the horizontal structure is bedding. The darker rocks in the steep cliffs are a sill, intruded at a lower level than the one that caps St Sunday Crag.

Descend to the valley floor, where the path joins a track from the east. Cross a bridge over Grisedale Beck and walk a short distance to a T-junction with the track which follows the southern side of the valley (NY 383 156). If you are in a hurry and do not mind walking beside a main road, turn left and follow this track down through woods to Grisedale Bridge and the A592 road, which leads south to Patterdale ½ km away.

Loc. **L51**, NY 385 157. In the woods below the track Grisedale Beck now flows in a gorge which drops steeply down to the Patterdale-Hartsop valley. In Ice Age times the Patterdale-Hartsop valley contained a larger glacier, which carved a deeper valley than did the Grisedale glacier. Consequently the Grisedale valley "hangs" above it. The gorge was eroded by a glacier-fed river, much larger and more powerful than the present **misfit** stream.

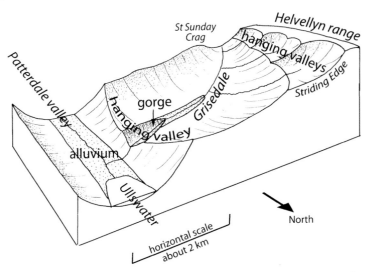

Fig. L51. Cartoon to show a hierarchy of glacial valleys. The corries on the east side of the Helvellyn range hang above the bigger valley of Grisedale. This in turn hangs above the still-deeper Patterdale valley.

For a more scenic route, turn right at the T-junction through a gate, follow the track up-valley for 50 metres and then turn left onto a path which leads uphill for 250 metres to a wall. Here turn left and follow the path to Patterdale through woods and parkland.

Loc. **L52**, NY 388 156. From hereabouts you can see north down Ullswater past the craggy volcanic terrain of Place Fell and Silver Crag.

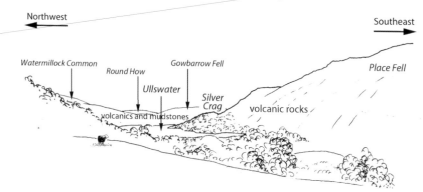

Fig. L52. View down Ullswater showing contrasted volcanic and mudstone scenery.

In the distance are the rounded hills of Gowbarrow Fell and Round How, composed of volcanics with mudstones. We last saw the mudstones at Loc. **L16**, and we shall cross them once more as we leave the Lake District.

JOURNAL 4 – PATTERDALE

WHAT DID THE VOLCANOES LOOK LIKE AND HOW DID THEY CHANGE OVER TIME?

We have now crossed most of the outcrop of volcanic rocks that forms the central Lake District. The total volume erupted was enormous – the pile of rocks was at least 6000 metres thick, covering the older Ordovician mudstones (Fig. **L16**), spreading over hundreds of square kilometres, and extending far beyond the area of the present Lake District. The rocks appear essentially as they would have looked at the time they were erupted (apart from later effects imposed on them, like cleavage and weathering). We have seen all the main rock-types that made up the volcanoes – lava, tuff, welded tuff, reworked tuff, breccia, and sills. Here we say a bit about how the volcanoes developed and what they may have looked like at different stages.

You probably found it difficult to keep track of all the different volcanic products along the line of the Walk. Many of the units can only be properly understood by studying their complete shapes in three dimensions, and it's only by detailed mapping of large areas that the historical sequence of events can be worked out. We will supplement the evidence we have seen on the Walk with information from studies of Lake District rocks by many geologists over many years.

It's important to realise that although the sequence of volcanic rocks on the Walk is in general terms from older to younger, the complexities of the volcanoes' plumbing mean that the rocks at successive localities are not necessarily in order of formation. Finally, as we've said before, the shapes of the volcanoes themselves have long since disappeared.

The lower half of the volcanic pile – from Ennerdale to Rosthwaite – was erupted as lavas and tuffs, and nearly all of them were erupted onto dry land. Evidence of erosion and re-deposition by water or landslides, in the form of reworked tuffs, was confined to small areas, such as would be found in low-lying places on the flanks of modern volcanoes. The volcanoes formed broad cones, as suggested in the next cartoon:

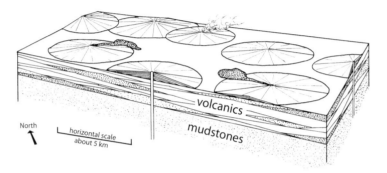

Cartoon showing how part of the Lake District might have looked towards the end of the first phase of the volcanic episode.

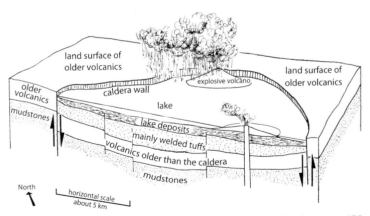

Cartoon showing the caldera part-way through its development 450 million years ago. Note that the welded tuffs and lake deposits are present only within the caldera. Some of the airborne tuffs spread onto the land surface outside the caldera.

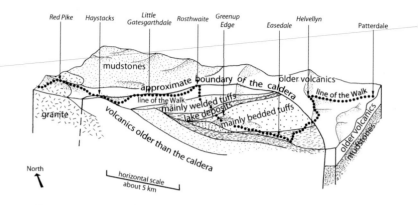

Cartoon showing the rocks of the central Lake District as they are at the present day. The shape of the caldera can be determined only by very detailed mapping and is not directly visible along the line of the Walk.

From Rosthwaite eastwards there are three significant changes in the volcanic rocks. Lavas virtually disappear, tuffs become the predominant rock, and reworking of the tuffs by water becomes much more widespread. The abundance of tuffs reflects a change to a much more violent style. Some individual explosive eruptions produced volumes of over 100 cubic kilometres – a stupendous amount, comparable to the 1815 eruption of Tambora, Indonesia, and ten times that erupted by Mt Pinatubo in 1991. The quantity of material erupted left the roof of the magma chambers below unsupported and the volcanic pile collapsed progressively, producing enormous circular depressions known as **calderas**. One was centred in the area of Scafell.

The caldera was at times occupied by a lake, and the tuffs that fell into it were subjected to reworking by currents or waves, as seen at Loc. **L33**. Many of the eruptions were ash flows of very hot gas and magma droplets, producing the welded tuffs at Locs **L27** and **L32**. (The water in the lake would have boiled near these eruptions.) Avalanches of loose material down steep slopes at the caldera margin produced breccias, as at Loc. **L37**. The caldera deposits are over 350 metres thick in places, so the basin existed for a substantial period, subsiding progressively to allow more deposits to accumulate. The distribution of the lake sediments gives us an idea of the caldera's size: it extended from Borrowdale in the north to Hardknott Pass in the south, and from Wasdale in the west to upper Grisedale in the east – an area of over 150 square kilometres.

Eventually the volcanism waned, and the remaining magma below the surface solidified as a large mass of coarse-grained crystalline rock. Some is now exposed as granite at Ennerdale (Loc. **L10**). Most is buried beneath the volcanics and we know its extent from geophysical measurements.

After the volcanism ceased the whole area subsided below sea level. This resulted in more marine sediments, of late Ordovician and Silurian age, being deposited on the eroded remains of the volcanic pile. These rocks (not seen on the line of the Walk) occupy the southern one-third of the Lake District, forming smoothly rounded hills which contrast with the craggy mountains of the volcanic central belt. The entire sequence of rocks in the Lake District was caught up in the **continental collision** which came later (Journal **5**).

The presence of a large mass of rigid crystalline granite protected the volcanic rocks above from the shortening effects of the continental collision. Consequently the volcanics, though cleaved and faulted, have been deformed relatively little, so most of the bedding is horizontal or gently dipping.

We shall see still more volcanic rocks in the next 20 km of the Walk. They continue the pattern of those we have seen up to now, with a few additional features which we discuss as we come to them.

WERE THE VOLCANIC ROCKS ERUPTED ON LAND OR IN THE SEA?

It's clear that water played an important part in producing the Lake District's volcanic rocks. We've seen that some of the ash fell in water, and some was moved around by water. But was it fresh- or sea-water? For many sedimentary rocks one can answer this question using fossils. The few fossils found in the volcanic rocks of the Lake District are of a microorganism that lived in fresh-water. So at least part of the volcanic succession was deposited above sea level. Today volcanic areas outside deserts and polar regions are colonised by plants, so one might expect to find land-plant fossils in our volcanics too – at least in the reworked tuffs which would have been transported during intervals in the volcanism. But land plants did not evolve till the Silurian period – several tens of millions of years later than our rocks.

HOW CAN WE DISTINGUISH A TUFF FROM A SEDIMENT?

By this stage of the walk you have come across plenty of examples of tuff, and we have confidently stated that these are volcanic. Yet many of their features – bedding, cross-bedding, graded bedding – are found in sedimentary rocks such as those we saw at St Bees. So how to tell the difference? The melting processes that produce magmas make a range of igneous rocks with compositions which are different from nearly all sedimentary rocks. The short distance of transport of volcanic products from igneous source to deposition as sediment in or near the volcano gave little chance for them to alter, so they retain their igneous composition. And because the rocks are still within the igneous environment it is best to regard them as volcanic.

WHY ARE THERE SO FEW LAVAS IN THE LAKE DISTRICT?

We need to think about the different plate-tectonic situations where volcanoes are found, illustrated in the next three drawings.

Hot spot volcano. These are places where the **mantle**, below the crust of the Earth, is particularly hot, and large amounts of magma are produced. Because the mantle is essentially dry, the lavas that are erupted are also dry and consequently gas-free. So they flow over the surface in a comparatively non-violent fashion. Travellers to active volcanic areas like Iceland and Hawaii will be familiar with the abundance of lava. There are plenty of examples of lava successions in ancient rocks too – in Washington State, the Deccan plateau in India, and on a smaller scale on the Scottish isles of Mull and Skye.

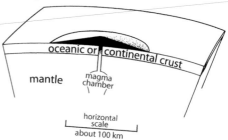

Hot spot volcano

Mid-ocean ridge volcanism. Here again the magma is derived from the mantle. Although erupted in the deep oceans, the magma cools so rapidly that it has no time to absorb water, and these eruptions also are non-violent. Iceland is a unique example of a hot spot coinciding with a mid-ocean ridge, with volcanoes erupting above sea level. Activity here can be explosive if the magma is erupted through a lake or glacier, like the eruption of Eyjafjallajökull in 2010.

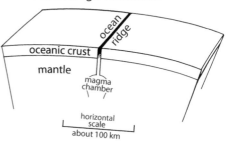

Mid-ocean ridge volcanism

Subduction-related volcanoes. In this situation **oceanic crust** of one tectonic plate is moved (subducted) below continental or oceanic crust of another plate. The subducted plate includes wet sediments of the original ocean floor, and water is incorporated into magmas that are produced in the subduction zone. It is this water, converted to steam, that powers the explosive eruptions that characterise the volcanoes in such places as the Andes, the Cascade Range of North America, and the islands of the eastern Caribbean. For a short but violent period 450 million years ago, the area which is now the Lake District lay over a subduction zone. The abundant tuffs (and a few lavas) that we have seen on the Walk reflect that tectonic situation.

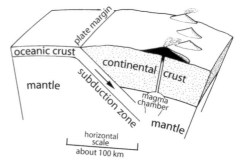

Subduction-related volcanoes

A further consequence of global plate movements was that, a few million years after the volcanic episode, the area of Britain became involved in a major collision of two continents. We continue the story in Journal **5**.

LANDFORM CONTRASTS ON HELVELLYN (Locs *L48, L51*)

As the drawing below shows, the eastern slopes of Helvellyn are carved into corries, but the western slopes descend smoothly to the Thirlmere valley. The prevailing wind direction during the Ice Age was, as now, from the west, and the snow that it carried accumulated preferentially on the sheltered eastern slopes, generating high-level glaciers which expanded downslope eastwards. Snow that fell on the western slopes would tend to be blown over the ridge, or avalanche down onto the Thirlmere glacier.

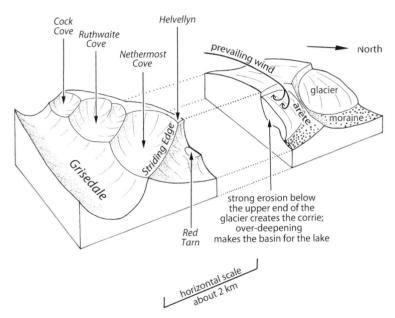

Helvellyn dissected. The right-hand portion shows the corries as they were when ice-filled; the left-hand portion shows them as they are today.

MOBILE MORAINES (Loc. *L42*)

When moraines are deposited they often contain unmelted ice left behind by the receding glacier. As the ice melts, the water produced can lubricate the mass of boulder clay making it mobile. If it is on a slope it may then move downwards as a coherent mass – an effect somewhere between a slow-moving avalanche and a landslide. This process would produce a lobe of boulder clay such as we see in Great Tongue. Its south-facing position exposed to warming by the Sun would have helped this process.

FAULTS AND THEIR SIGNIFICANCE (Loc. *L33*)

The fault in the boulder at Loc. **L33** might seem to be such a small feature that we could ignore it. However, it shows in miniature many characteristics of much larger faults – small really is beautiful! So we start with a general statement that applies to faults (and folds) on any scale from pocket-sized to mountain chains:

A **fault** is the response of rock to deformation by brittle fracture followed by relative movement of the blocks of rock on the two sides of the break. When rocks are faulted all the deformation occurs on the fault plane, with the rocks each side unaffected. Ductile (plastic) deformation produces a **fold**, and the deformation is distributed over a large volume of rock. Whether a rock deforms in a brittle or ductile manner depends on several factors, including the temperature and how quickly (or slowly) the deforming forces are applied. In general, faulting is the more common style of deformation at shallow, cooler levels in the Earth's crust.

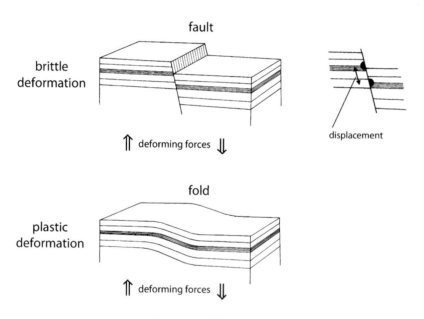

Fault and fold contrasted.

A fault plane is usually much weaker than the rocks each side of it and can remain weak for millions of years; this is the reason why faults and the immediately adjacent rocks are so often easily eroded, making the exact position of the fault difficult to find. In the case of the boulder at Loc. **L33** the fault resolidified and is now as strong as the rest of the rock – rather like a wound healed with scar tissue – and another feature that makes this little fault so easy to study.

The size of a fault can be estimated from the amount of relative movement, or **displacement**, of the blocks each side of the fault plane (see the drawing above).

Prolonged deformation can result in very large displacement (tens, hundreds, or thousands of metres), while the adjacent blocks remain relatively undeformed. Present-day earthquakes are usually related to continued movement on long-established faults.

There is still more information to be gleaned from the detailed shape of a fault. Imagine a slab of layer-cake. Push the two ends of the slab towards each other. If the slab is ductile it will bend, forming a fold. But the case we want to consider here is brittle deformation, resulting in faulting. Because the slab is under compression the material on one side of the fault rides up over the other, as in the upper drawing below. So the direction in which the fault slopes – its dip – is towards the block that moves upwards. This is characteristic of faults produced by lateral compression.

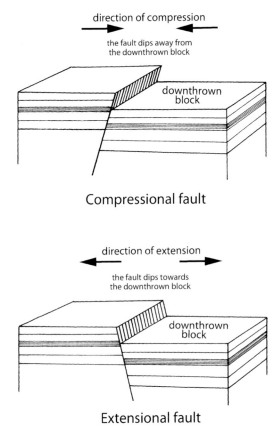

Compressional and extensional faults.

Pulling the layers apart along their length also makes a fault, but in this case the fault dips towards the block that moves downwards – an extensional fault, and the opposite of the previous situation. So the angular relationship of the dipping fault to the layers it cuts tells us about the system of stresses that the layers were exposed to. This might seem a trivial conclusion for a layer cake, but on the scale of mountain-building the systematic study of fault patterns gives valuable information for understanding the forces that formed them. And in the search for mineral resources faults can greatly influence the potential value of a resource.

PUZZLES AT BIRKS (Loc. *L33*)

Puzzle I. Evidence for water

Clues can be found in Areas 1 and 2 of Fig. **L33/1**. In Area 1 there is an erosion surface which cuts across the coarse ash layers below. Layering in the two hollows at the right-hand end drapes up the sides and over the high point in between. The order of events was: 1) coarse ash was deposited; 2) erosion (scouring) partly removed the coarse ash; 3) fine ash was deposited in thin layers, gradually filling the hollows and draping over the high points.

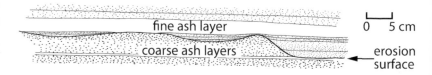

detail : layers drape over the high point

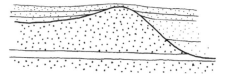

Area 1. Scoured surface with later infilling.

In Area 2 the top of the coarse ash layers is a rippled surface. The bed above is a very thin layer of pale-coloured very-fine-grained ash that is draped over the ripples. The order of events was: 1) coarse ash was deposited; 2) waves caused ripples to form on its top surface; 3) mud-grade ash settled out of suspension onto the rippled surface; 4) fine ash was deposited on the mud-draped ripples.

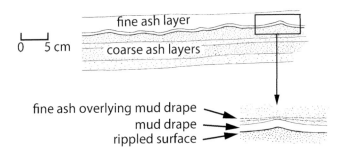

Area 2. Rippled surface draped with fine ash.

The mud drape in Area 2 is the key evidence. Such drapes form only under water where mud in suspension settles out when the waves die down.

Puzzle 2. Right-way-up?

The erosion surface in Area 1 and the draping of the layers over the ripples in Area 2 mean that the layers are the right way up as we see them in the boulder.

You may recall at Loc. **L3** a discussion of graded bedding and its use for telling way-up in sedimentary rocks. Volcanoes are less regular in their performance than sediments in water. In fact size-grading in ash deposits can form in either direction – getting finer upwards or getting coarser upwards. So graded bedding can't be used to determine way-up in volcanic rocks.

Discussion of way-up may seem trivial in the Lake District, where the rocks are all right-way-up and few have dips of more than 45 degrees. However, in mountain belts such as the Himalaya and the Scottish Highlands large-scale folding was so intense that some layers have been turned upside-down; so tests for way-up are very useful for working out the detailed structure.

Puzzle 3. How long?

This is problematic, even for an experienced volcanologist (which neither of us is). Volcanoes are places where material is deposited very rapidly, so a time-span of thousands of years is unlikely. Modern volcanoes do go through dormant phases lasting centuries. Whether the time-span was hours, days, months, years, or centuries is hard to establish. In Area 2 the edge of the scour is very steep, but there is no sign of slumping of the scour sides, so the coarse ash bed must have been compacted before the scouring occurred – implying a gap of weeks or months at least.

Puzzle 4. The fault

The amount by which the lowest bed is displaced by the fault is greater than that of the highest bed. In fact the displacement decreases progressively from bottom to top, as in the diagram below. This suggests that the fault was moving *while the ash was being deposited*. The downward motion of the left-hand block created more space for ash to accumulate to the left of the fault than to the right. This resulted in a greater total thickness at left than at right.

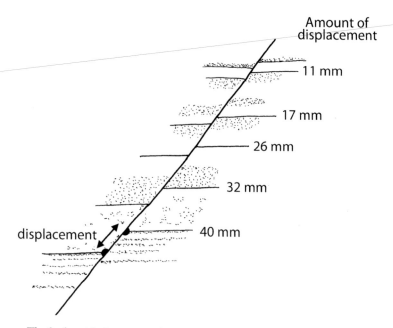

The fault, with the measured amounts of displacement of some of the beds.

Why should this happen in volcanic rocks? A volcano is an inherently unstable feature, with magma moving spasmodically upwards to erupt ashes and lavas on the surface. One of the results of withdrawal of magma from below or lowering of upward pressure is to produce local subsidence within the volcanic structure. Different parts of the volcano will subside at different rates, and faults – at any scale from centimetres to tens of metres – record this.

Let's now look at the geometry of the fault in Fig. **L33/1**. The dip of the fault is to the left, towards the downward-moving block. This is a feature of an *extensional* fault. So we can conclude that the part of the volcano where the ash at Loc. **L33** was deposited was under lateral extension at that time. Not a very profound conclusion, you might say, given the small scale. However, the principle has important applications for monitoring modern volcanoes, where stress meters recording small changes of extension or compression are used to predict impending eruptions.

Puzzle 5. Lack of rounding

The answer lies in the short distance of transport – the source outcrops for the rocks are only a few hundred metres away. Birks is very close to the central watershed of the Lake District, and the glaciers flowed down valleys that radiate out from here like the spokes of a wheel. So any ice-transported rocks must come from close by.

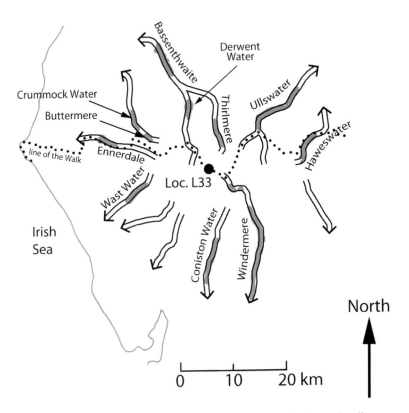

Map showing the radial pattern of the Lake District's glaciers and valleys, with Loc. L33 close to the centre.

We hope you have enjoyed these puzzles and finding out their answers. They do have a serious point too – it is often the very small features in rocks that provide the information about how they were formed and in what environment. It's a principle with wide applications – as one example, study of the fine detail in photos and images from distant planets helps us to understand how they were formed.

THE WALK – PATTERDALE TO SHAP

From the Patterdale Hotel take the Ambleside road and in about 100 metres at NY 398 158 turn left down a lane. After 300 metres turn left in the small settlement of Rooking. Where the tarmac ends bear right up a steep rough track to a junction with a footpath. Turn right on a well-graded path signposted "Boredale Hause and Angle Tarn". In 200 metres, near a metal bench beside a stream, Rooking Gill, the path divides. Follow the left fork of the path for a further 250 metres.

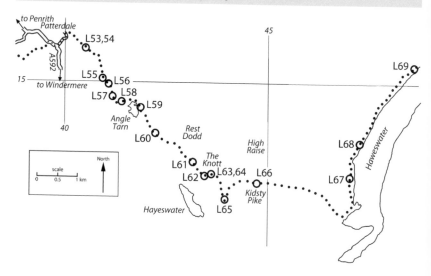

Patterdale to Haweswater.

VIOLENT ERUPTIONS CONTINUE

Loc. **L53**, NY 405 159. Beside the path, upslope from the southern end of a row of larch trees, is a small exposure of darkish grey tuff, with prominent near-vertical cleavage. From here for the next 200 metres or so are numerous small tuff exposures, all cleaved and some with grains up to 2 mm across, but with no discernible layering.

Continue for another 100 metres.

Loc. **L54**, NY 405 158. Pink-weathering rocks are exposed above the join of the paths.

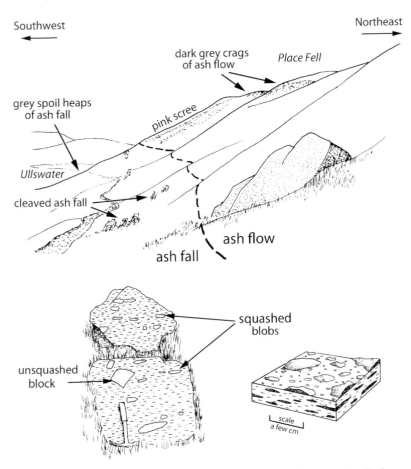

Fig. L54. Welded tuffs beside the path. The lower drawing shows detail of the rocks on the right of the top picture and an idealised impression of blobs squashed into disc-shapes.

The vertical faces have a streaky structure, with lozenges up to 20 cm across in a matrix of much smaller but similar shapes. These are welded tuffs, which we first saw at Loc. **L18**. You may recall that the lozenge shapes were formed in an ash flow by the squashing of semi-liquid blobs. If you view the exposure from the top you can see that the lozenges have roughly circular outlines, so in three dimensions they are discs. As at **L18**, the orientation of the discs tells us the original horizontal – here roughly the same as the present.

Now look back the way you have come. At the top of the slope below the summit of Place Fell are grey crags. The grey colour is due to lichen cover; the true rock colour is pink, as can be seen in the screes below each exposure, which are lichen-free. With your eye follow the screes down the hillside and notice that the colour changes about level with where you are standing. Below this level the screes are grey and the rock exposures cleaved like those we saw on the path. This allows us to sketch in a (roughly horizontal) contact between the two rock units, cleaved tuff below and pink ash flow above.

> *Continue up the path to Boredale Hause, NY 407 157, from which a stream, Stonebarrow Gill, flows westwards into the Patterdale valley. Follow the stream eastwards and then southwards along a cairned path. The next Location is 1 km ahead.*

Over the next ½ km occasional pathside exposures are cleaved tuff. However, the pink rocks that litter the path suggest that another ash flow is close by.

Loc. **L55**, NY 409 151. Here two closely spaced cairns mark the headwaters of Stonebarrow Gill, west of Stony Rigg. The screes above the path are composed of the pink rock seen before, here eroded from exposures of ash flow above. So, from Rooking to Stony Rigg the rock succession from bottom up is: tuff – welded tuff – tuff – welded tuff. Fig. **L55** gives an impression of what conditions were like during eruptions.

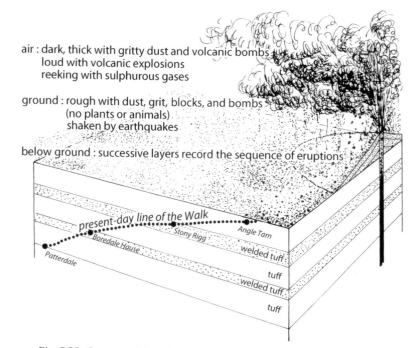

air : dark, thick with gritty dust and volcanic bombs
    loud with volcanic explosions
    reeking with sulphurous gases

ground : rough with dust, grit, blocks, and bombs
    (no plants or animals)
    shaken by earthquakes

below ground : successive layers record the sequence of eruptions

present-day line of the Walk
Angle Tarn
Stony Rigg
welded tuff
Boredale Hause
Patterdale
tuff
welded tuff
tuff

*Fig. **L55**. Cartoon of the volcanic succession and an eruption in progress.*

Walk on for ½ km. Where the path divides, at the head of the steep gully of Dubhow Beck, take the higher eastern branch, with views of Angletarn Pikes to the left. Angletarn Pikes has two summits, north and south, 200 metres apart, separated by lower ground.

LAVAS AGAIN

Loc. **L56**, NY 413 147. West of the northern summit of Angletarn Pikes. The screes near the path – a convenient sample of the rocks above – are pitted like some of the tuffs that we have seen earlier. But a freshly broken specimen viewed in bright sunlight reveals crystals which flash in sunlight – rather than tuff particles, which would not. So the rocks must have formed from a coherent mass of magma, as in a lava. The rocks rise in tiers separated by grassy ledges, each ledge representing the top of a lava flow.

*Fig. **L56**. Tuff and lava on the north summit of Angletarn Pikes.*

A short detour to the south summit of Angletarn Pikes east of the path provides more evidence that the brown-weathering rocks are lavas.

Loc. **L57**, NY 414 147. Crags on the northern side of the south summit of Angletarn Pikes. Here the rocks contain two types of joint.

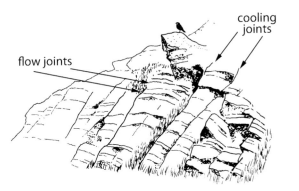

*Fig. **L57**. Joints in lava, viewed from below the crag.*

The near-horizontal joints result from **flow-banding**, formed when the lava was moving, as at Loc. **L20**. The vertical joints were formed during cooling and contraction of the lava after it had stopped moving.

Loc. **L58**, NY 414 146. Stop on the path at the point where Angle Tarn first comes into view and look at the rocky slope above the path on the left.

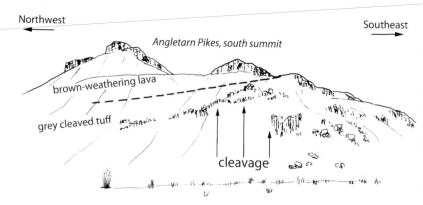

*Fig. **L58**. Lava overlying cleaved tuff, Angletarn Pikes, south summit.*

Follow the path for another ½ km round the east side of Angle Tarn and pause for a view across to Cat Crag.

Loc. **L59**, NY 419 144, or any point with a view of Angle Tarn. Cat Crag on the west side of Angle Tarn is also composed of tuff, though you can't tell this from here. What you can see is layering – the horizontal ledges that cross the crags are the tops of individual tuff beds. Also obvious is nearly vertical cleavage.

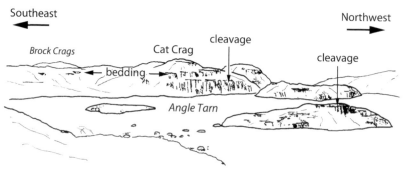

*Fig. **L59**. Cat Crag and Angle Tarn from the east.*

From Angle Tarn to Loc. L64 the route continues over cleaved tuff, locally stained red by iron-rich groundwaters. The next location is in 300 metres.

MORE VOLCANIC ROCKS AND SOME FINE GLACIAL VALLEYS

Loc. **L60**, NY 422 138. Two prominent posts mark an old fence line. Hereabouts there is much peat. Where walkers' feet have worn it away, the tuff bedrock is white due to leaching by acids in the peat. To the northeast there is a fine view down the broad **U**-shaped valley of Bannerdale, its floor littered with subdued moraine hummocks.

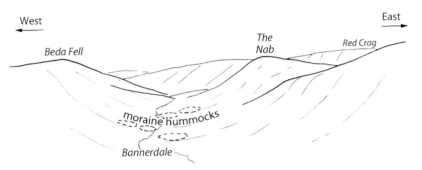

Fig. L60. Bannerdale from near Angle Tarn.

Continue on the path for another 1½ km to Sulphury Gill (NY 432 132), with views of Hayeswater to the right. Cross a wall and continue upwards towards The Knott.

Loc. **L61**, NY 433 130. Over the next 200 metres look in the path for pieces of a smooth medium-grey rock with white patches. This is lava.

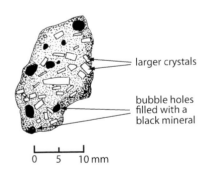

larger crystals

bubble holes filled with a black mineral

0 5 10 mm

Fig. L61. A lava, with large straight-sided crystals, indicating two stages of cooling on the way to the surface of the Earth, and with rounded bubble holes (now infilled with a dark mineral), indicating eruption when the pressure was released at the surface. For entertainment you could count the number of stages of Earth history you can see in this one small pebble!

Continue for 300 metres to a sharp leftward bend in the path.

Loc. **L62**, NY 434 128. About 30 metres above the bend is a prominent blocky exposure surmounted by a ruinous wall. This is another very coarse tuff. No layering is visible in the exposure but loose blocks below show fine layering, suggesting that some of this tuff was transported by water.

Walk on for 200 metres to where the path crosses an extremely straight wall.

Loc. **L63**, NY 436 128. Look in the path near here for pale rocks with wispy dark streaks. These are welded tuffs, the streaks being much flattened semi-liquid blobs.

Loc. **L64**, NY 437 127. A diversion to the summit of The Knott gives a fine view of Hayeswater Gill and the delta that has formed at its entry to Hayeswater.

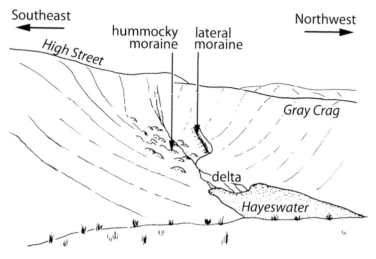

*Fig. **L64**. Hayeswater from The Knott.*

The valley floor south of the lake is littered with hummocky moraine, and on the west side is a fine example of a lateral moraine – a ridge of debris sloping diagonally down valley, deposited at the margin of a glacier from debris falling from above.

Return to the path and follow it SSE till it joins another from the north, ½ km ahead.

A NEXUS OF VALLEYS AND A ROMAN ROUTE

Loc. **L65**, NY 439 123. The Straits of Riggindale.

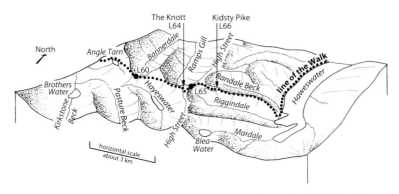

*Fig. **L65**. Cartoon (an oblique aerial view from the southeast) of the valleys and ridges centred on The Knott. Many of the ridges are arêtes like Striding Edge on Helvellyn. Some of the higher ridges are narrow but flat-topped, suggesting that glaciers occupied the valleys but did not form a continuous ice-sheet covering the whole area.*

High Street was the line of a Roman Road. Its elevated and exposed route was preferable to travelling through thickly wooded valleys below – an indication of how much the scenery has changed in **2000** years.

From Loc. **L65** you can see the length of Riggindale, again with U-shaped profile and subdued moraine hummocks on its floor. The profile is in fact asymmetrical: the slopes of Riggindale Crag to the right are steeper than those of Kidsty Pike to the left. This may be caused by the rocks of Riggindale Crag having been more resistant to weathering and erosion, due for example to more widely spaced joints and less cleavage.

*The next Location is 1 km ahead. From Loc. **L65** take the path to the north, swinging progressively to the east round the head of Riggindale over scattered exposures of cleaved tuff. If visibility is poor, ½ km ahead be careful to avoid the left turn northward along the Roman route to High Raise and beyond.*

A HIGH POINT

Loc. **L66**, NY 447 126. Kidsty Pike, the highest point of the "standard" Coast-to-Coast route and a superb viewpoint. Straight across the valley is Rigindale Crag. To the east one can see the top end of Haweswater and on a clear day the Pennines beyond.

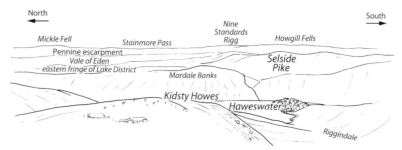

*Fig. **L66**. The view east from Kidsty Pike. In the far distance (35-40 km away) is the Pennine escarpment, with the Howgill Fells to the right. The Vale of Eden lies between the Pennines and the Lake District. The route of the Walk goes over Nine Standards Rigg.*

Descend the broad ridge eastwards 1½ km to Kidsty Howes and thence southeastward to the point where Riggindale Beck enters Haweswater. From here the route follows the western shore of the reservoir. Turn left, cross the footbridge over Randale Beck and follow the path for 1 km, passing below the lichen-covered tuff exposures of Flakehow Crags, to Castle Crag, the site of an Iron Age fort.

MORE WELDED TUFF

Loc. **L67**, NY 470 128. A broad grassy terrace at the top of a rise in the path below Castle Crag provides a good viewpoint.

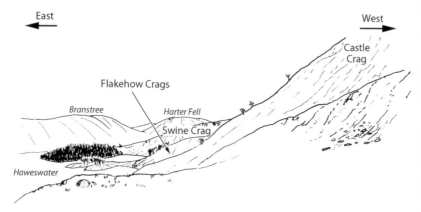

*Fig. **L67**. The view south from below Castle Crag.*

To the south beyond the broken ground of Flakehow Crags is Swine Crag, the easterly continuation of Riggindale Crag. This separates Riggindale and Mardale, the two major valleys that drain into the south end of Haweswater. Close above you to the west is the steep cliff of Castle Crag. In contrast to Flakehow Crags, the rocks are uncleaved with widely spaced joints and a scree of large blocks below. Inspection of the scree reveals the rock to be welded tuff with flattened discs up to 5 cm across.

Continue on the path for ½ km, noting nearly horizontal crag-and-ledge features in Whelter Crags on the western skyline. Cross Whelter Beck, passing a small larch plantation on the right of the path, opposite a tower on the eastern lakeshore. Stop at the foot of the cliff above the path, 200 metres north of the plantation.

A DOLERITE INTRUSION

Loc. **L68**, NY 474 136, Whelter Knotts.

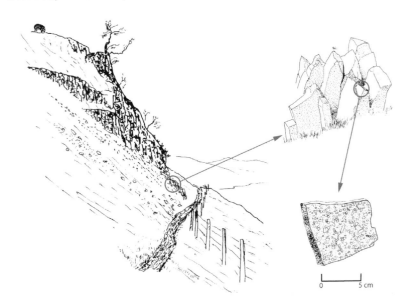

*Fig. **L68**. Dolerite at Whelter Knotts. The insets show two levels of detail.*

The rocks close above the path are brown-weathering (where not lichen-covered), with widely spaced joints and no bedding or cleavage. The surface is rough, suggesting that the rock is relatively coarse-grained. Freshly broken fragments on the path have white crystals, many with straight edges. The brown colour is similar to that of the lavas at Angletarn Pikes, but the overall grain size is coarser. So the rock must have cooled and crystallised more slowly than a lava erupted at the surface. In other words it is an intrusion, part of the volcanoes' plumbing. The rock is a **dolerite**, a coarser-grained equivalent of a basalt.

> *Follow the path for 2½ km to Measand Beck, passing occasional exposures of brown rock.*

MORE DOLERITE

Loc. **L69**, NY 487 154. Fifty metres south of Measand Beck at the junction of the Route with a path descending from the hillside to the west, close to a lone pine tree.

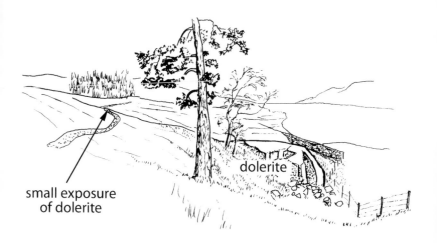

*Fig. **L69**. Dolerite exposures south of Measand Beck.*

From here to Measand Beck bridge the route crosses exposures of moderately coarse-grained crystalline rock with white crystals several millimetres across. This is another dolerite. All the exposures of volcanic rocks we have seen since leaving Patterdale were erupted on the surface, except for the dolerites (Locs **L68** and **L69**), which were intruded as sills low down in the volcanic system.

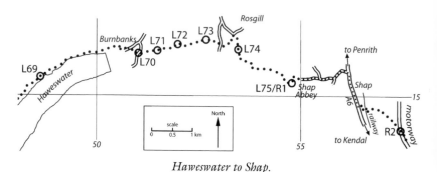

Haweswater to Shap.

Continue on the path for another 2 km. Keep an eye on the dam through the trees, and 400 metres after you pass it, look for a gated path downhill to the right. Descend through trees to Burnbanks, a settlement on the site of the dam-builders' accommodation. At its east end turn right off the road by a parking space at a Coast-to-Coast sign. The path winds through woods strewn with large rounded mossy boulders – all that remains of moraine dumped by a retreating glacier, most of the finer particles having been winnowed out by streams.

Naddle Bridge, with the modern bridge behind.

Loc. **L70**, NY 510 160. Naddle Bridge. Cross the bridge and follow the south bank of the river. In the river downstream of the bridge are more boulders, again rounded but a good deal smaller than those just seen in the wood. These are small enough to have been carried by water – either the present river or its more vigorous glacier-fed predecessor.

THE LAST OF THE VOLCANICS

Loc. **L71**, NY 515 160. Park Bridge. Fifty metres south of the path is a rocky ledge sloping downwards towards the path. The surface has been smoothed by ice, but close-up it is rough: a coarse tuff and the last volcanic rock we shall see on the Walk.

Four hundred metres east of Park Bridge the river bends north, but the Route diverges eastward to a gate next to a deep gully which drains the fields to the southeast of it.

BOULDER CLAY AND POST-GLACIAL STREAMS

Loc. **L72**, NY 520 162, by the small bridge over the gully.

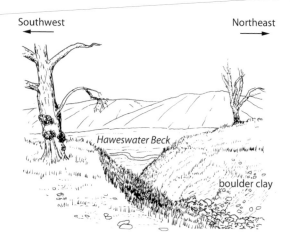

Southwest ← → Northeast

Haweswater Beck

boulder clay

*Fig. **L72**. Boulder clay is exposed in the east bank of the gully.*

This thick deposit was left behind by the ice of the Haweswater glacier as it spread out from the Haweswater valley. The situation mirrors what we saw in Ennerdale on the other side of the mountains, where the low ground to the west is similarly mantled by boulder clay (see the second drawing in Journal **1**). In both cases the predominant process in the narrow valley glacier is erosion, making the characteristic **U**-shaped profile. As the glacier spreads onto the lowland, erosion virtually ceases. When the glacier eventually melts, its load of rocky material is deposited as boulder clay. As we saw in Journal **3**, the volume of eroded rock from the highlands matches the volume of deposits on the lowland.

The contrast between areas of erosion and of deposition continues to the present day in the action of streams and rivers. Haweswater Beck is spreading a floodplain on the flat valley floor, while its small tributary is eroding a **V**-shaped gully into the steeper valley sides.

This location provides a distant view of the country ahead. Beneath your feet the bedrock is still Ordovician, but on the skyline to the northeast the rocks are Carboniferous – 100 million years younger. We illustrate the view at the next Location.

> *Go through the gate and turn right uphill along the edge of the field to Highpark and then across fields for 500 metres to a high point.*

APPROACHING THE END OF THE LAKE DISTRICT, AND A PREVIEW OF THE NEXT STAGE

Loc. **L73**, NY 527 163. Pause here for a fine view.

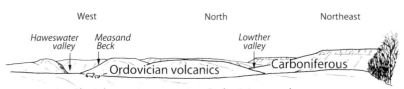

Fig. **L73**. *Panoramic view from near Rawhead.*

To the west are the steep slopes north of Haweswater, cut by the V-shaped valley of Measand Beck. These and the rocky bracken-covered distant slopes to the north are underlain by volcanics. In the foreground are fields mantled with boulder clay – evidenced by the smooth surface and lack of bedrock exposure. Any projecting boulders have been removed and built into walls.

To the northeast, and continuing to the right of the view, are Carboniferous **limestones**. Just below the skyline on a clear day you can pick out nearly horizontal bands, which represent the limestone bedding. You can also see the pale grey limestone in the numerous walls that criss-cross the hillside. At the base of the slope but hidden at this viewpoint is the River Lowther, which marks the eastern edge of the Lake District rocks and the base of the Carboniferous. We shall see this significant boundary exposed at Loc. **L75**.

The next Location is 1½ km ahead. Continue eastward across the field to pass buildings at Rawhead on your left. Cross an unfenced gravel track and in 100 metres turn left downslope through boggy ground to the River Lowther at Rosgill Bridge. Do not cross the bridge, but turn sharp right on a farm track parallel to the river for 100 metres to where the track curves right and starts to climb. Leave the track, cross a stile to its left, and follow the path for 400 metres to rocky exposures sticking out of the valley floor to the right of the path southeast of Goodcroft.

FAIRY CRAG AND SOME PUZZLING ROCKS

Loc. **L74**, NY 535 161. Fairy Crag, a group of rounded ridges trending northwest-southeast. This is one of the more unusual exposures you will see on the Walk, and worth spending a bit of time at, if the weather is fine. We suggest that you try to locate examples of the three rock-types shown in the drawing – granite, mudstone, and quartz veins – and look for the evidence for their relative ages. We explain things in more detail in the Journal.

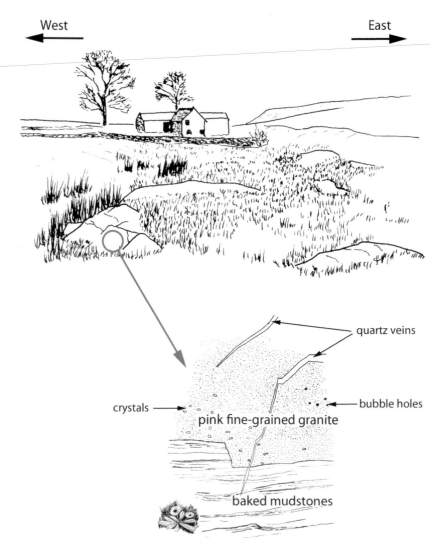

West

East

quartz veins

crystals

bubble holes

pink fine-grained granite

baked mudstones

Fig. L74. Fairy Crag. The inset is a composite drawing of some of the essential features of the exposure.

Rejoin the path and cross Swindale Beck by the charming Parish Crag packhorse bridge. From here the route trends southeastwards to Shap Abbey through fields with no rock exposure, due to boulder clay cover. Climb 400 metres to ruinous farm buildings, cross the farmyard and exit onto a track through stiles at the southern corner. In 150 metres turn left onto a path signposted 'Shap'. The path curves gently right for 500 metres, crossing two walls, and then descends over boggy boulder-strewn ground to a third wall, overlooking the River Lowther. From here you can see the ruins of Shap Abbey upstream. Turn right and follow the path for 300 metres and cross the river by the old Abbey Bridge to a small car park. An important Location is in the river bank on the upstream side of the near end of the new bridge.

THE END OF ONE CHAPTER OF EARTH HISTORY, THE BEGINNING OF THE NEXT

Loc. **L75/R1**, NY 548 153, below the north end of the newer bridge leading to Shap Abbey. See the drawing on page 108.

Geologically, this exposure is the most significant in the whole length of the Walk. It definitively marks the end of the rocks of the Lake District, with their history of volcanism followed by continental collision, and the beginning of the less-eventful story of the younger rocks which extend from here all the way to the east coast.

The boundary between the strongly deformed Lower Palaeozoic rocks and the overlying Upper Palaeozoic rocks has a total length of about 350 km in northern England and southern Scotland. In all that distance there are only half-a-dozen good exposures, and this is one of them. So we must make the most of it!

The **unconformity** is the surface between the folded dark purple-brown Ordovician mudstones in the lower half of the exposure, and the undeformed nearly horizontal grey-green Carboniferous beds with angular purple-brown pebbles in the upper half. It is a 360-million-year-old land surface, and there is a time-gap of 110 million years between the older and the younger layers – well worth spending a few minutes to ponder!

This fairly complicated exposure is explained in detail in Journal **5**.

Take the footpath directly uphill to the gateway at the top.

From the gate you can see how the change of rock-type affects the scenery. Contrast the irregular, rough fields covering the Lower Palaeozoic mudstones west of Shap Abbey with the rectangular, flatter fields of richer grass on Carboniferous limestones to the east.

The next Location is 4 km ahead. Continue the Walk to Shap village. A footpath in the fields on the left of the road passes Skellaw Hill (Hill of Skulls) barrow (part of an extensive archaeological site about 4000 years old). At the main A6 road, turn right and walk through the village for 1 km. To continue the Walk, look for Moss Grove to the left near the south end of the village.

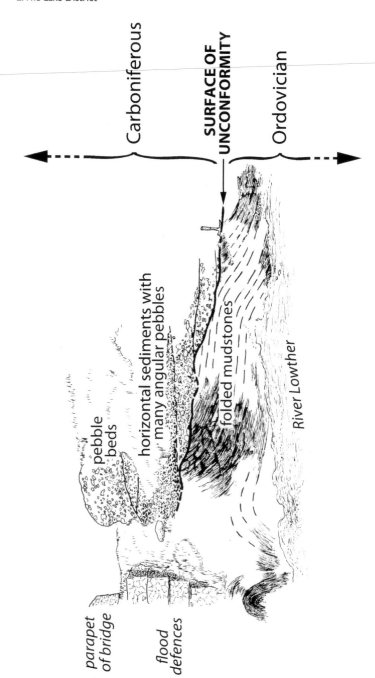

Carboniferous

SURFACE OF
UNCONFORMITY

Ordovician

pebble
beds

horizontal sediments with
many angular pebbles

folded mudstones

River Lowther

parapet
of bridge

flood
defences

Fig. L75/R1. The exposure below the bridge at Shap Abbey, viewed from river level. (Loose rubble and other superficial features are largely omitted from the drawing, and dashed lines suggest the shape of the bedrock where it's not exposed.)

JOURNAL 5 – SHAP

FAIRY CRAG: LAVA OR SOMETHING ELSE? (Loc. *L74*)

The dark grey mudstones, finely layered in places, occur mostly near the sides of the ridges. We last saw these rocks west of the Lake District at Angler's Crag (Locs **L8** and **L9**). The pinkish rock forms the central areas of the ridges. It contains crystals, in a matrix that is homogeneous and unlayered – features of an igneous rock. The rounded pits are bubble holes formed in rising liquid magma as it neared the surface. All this fits with the rock being a lava, interlayered with the mudstones, and with a two-stage cooling history, like the lavas at Locs **L17** and **L61**.

But is the pink rock a lava? The contacts between it and the mudstones provide the key evidence. Interlayered lava and mudstones would have contacts that run parallel to the mudstone layering. But at Fairy Crag the margins of the pink rock *cut across* the mudstone layering. This means that it was *intruded* into the mudstone; so it is younger. Because the intrusion's outcrop is long and narrow, and the contacts with the mudstone are nearly vertical, it is a **dyke**, like the one at Loc. **L9** but wider (see Journal **2**, Volcanic Rocks, Drawing **a**). The crystals – quartz (square and glassy) and feldspar (rectangular and whitish) – and the pale matrix make it a granite. The white veins are quartz, formed from hot groundwaters circulating through cracks (as at Loc. **L21**). They cut across both mudstone and granite, so are younger than both.

THE CALEDONIAN UNCONFORMITY (Loc. *L75/R1*)

The **unconformity** is the boundary between the deformed Lower Palaeozoic and the younger Carboniferous rocks. It is the land surface that resulted from erosion of the rocks of the Lake District after the collision of continents that created the Caledonian mountains (from Caledonia – an old name for Scotland).

To understand the significance of the exposure of the unconformity at Shap Abbey (and the rest of the outcrop of which it is representative) we can start by looking at the ages of the rocks. The pebble beds above the unconformity date from early in the Carboniferous – 360 million years old. The mudstones below the unconformity were deposited about 470 million years ago, and deformed around 420 million years ago.

The difference in the ages of the older and the younger rocks at Shap Abbey is 110 million years. It takes only a moment to say it, but geologically it was a very long time. Contrast it, for instance, with the 65 million years between the extinction of the dinosaurs and the present day. Think of all that has happened in that time, including the building of the Alps and Himalayas, and the evolution of most of the plants and animals that we know today.

The deformation of the older rocks resulted from the collision of two ancient continents, as shown in the drawing on the next page.

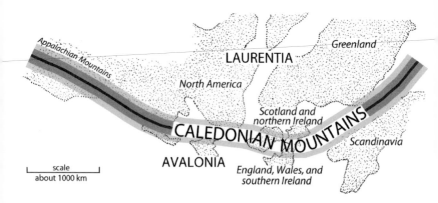

Simplified map showing parts of the Laurentian and Avalonian continents and the Caledonian mountains that developed from their collision. Present-day land areas are shown in their approximate relative positions as they were at the time of the collision. (The present-day Atlantic Ocean did not develop until much later – see Chapter 7).

The southern continent, known as Avalonia, comprised most of England and Wales, the southern part of Ireland, southern Newfoundland, and parts of the southeast coasts of Canada and the United States. Western Scandinavia was involved in the collision too, though it belonged to a different tectonic plate. The larger northern continent, Laurentia, included Scotland and the northern part of Ireland, and also Greenland, most of Canada, and much of the United States. In between arose a mountain belt stretching from the North Sea through Scotland to the Appalachians.

We all know the devastating effects of the impact of two moving vehicles; the collision of two continents takes place over millions of years and has much bigger effects. The collision zone in northern Britain was up to 500 km wide, with the Lake District near its southeastern edge. The continental crust increased in thickness from about 30 km to perhaps twice as much. The rocks were intensely deformed. Granites and other igneous rocks were produced because of the increased temperatures. The process of the mountain-building was spread over 100 million years; the Lake District was most affected towards the end of that period, at about 420 million years ago.

The boundary, or join, between the two continents is a structure called the Iapetus **Suture**. Its outcrop is largely covered by younger rocks, but it can be mapped in depth geophysically and is known to run across northern England from the Solway Firth (Fig. L4/2) to the North Sea coast near Berwick.

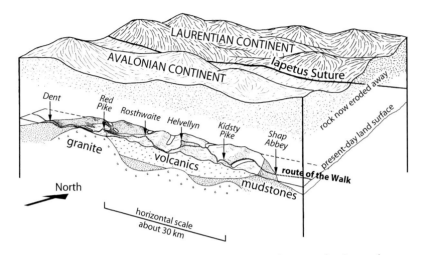

An impression of the area of the Caledonian mountain range that is now the Lake District. The top surface shows parts of the two former continents and the Iapetus Suture, as they might have been just after the continental collision. The lower part of the drawing shows the route of the Walk and the present-day land surface, with the underlying structure. An enormous amount of rock has been eroded away in the 400 million years since the collision.

Just like growing mountain belts such as the Himalayas today, the new mountains were being eroded as they were formed. The erosion produced vast quantities of sediment – the well-known Old Red Sandstone, of Devonian age, was deposited over wide areas of Scotland, England, and Wales. (In south Asia the analogue is the accumulation of sediment, tens of kilometres thick, in the wide plain of the Indus and Ganges on the south side of the Himalayas.) Probably Devonian sediments were deposited on the unconformity at Loc. **L75/R1** and then eroded, before the Carboniferous.

You can place your finger on the 360-million-year-old land surface. At the beginning of the Carboniferous the surface would have been warm, or even hot, as Britain was at this time near the Equator. There were streams running over it, carrying pebbles eroded from the underlying mudstones. The new chapter of Earth history begins at the moment when the streams slowed down and erosion of the land surface changed to deposition onto it. From then on for the next 60 million years Carboniferous sediments dominate the story, and will continue until we get to Richmond at the east side of the Yorkshire Dales.

A lasting effect of all the processes that happened to the rocks during the Caledonian mountain-building was that they became essentially rigid and difficult to deform any further. The rocks continue to the east as a stable **basement** to all of the younger sediments. We will find that rumblings from below-stairs influenced the upper layers in a variety of ways. More of that later.

A (VERY) SIMPLIFIED HISTORY OF THE LAKE DISTRICT – THE DEATH OF AN OCEAN AND THE BIRTH OF A MOUNTAIN CHAIN

470 million years ago (early Ordovician) – mudstones in a deep ocean

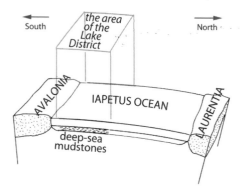

The area which is now the Lake District was on the south side of a wide but narrowing ocean (Iapetus Ocean) which lay between two continents, a small one named Avalonia and a much larger one named Laurentia. A thick sequence of mudstones was deposited on the ocean floor (Loc. **L3**). These sediments now occupy the northern one-third of the Lake District.

450 million years ago (late Ordovician) – a lively episode of volcanic activity

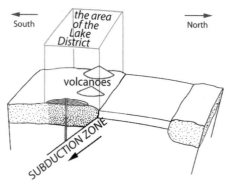

The Iapetus Ocean was getting narrower because the **oceanic crust** was being subducted below Avalonia. **Magma** which was formed in the **subduction zone** (Journal **4**) produced big volcanoes in the area of the Lake District. The volcanism started with lavas and tuffs (Locs **L12** to **L20**), and continued with spectacular explosive eruptions in a large **caldera** (Locs **L27** to **L39**). The volcanics form the central one-third of the Lake District, and were the principal theme of our Walk. The Ennerdale granite is closely related to the volcanics.

430 million years ago (early Silurian) – sediments in a shallow sea

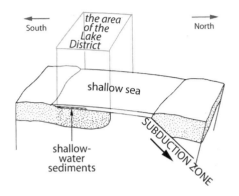

The north side of Avalonia sank below sea level. Shallow-water sediments were deposited covering the now-extinct volcanoes. These sediments (we did not see them on the line of the Walk) make the southern one-third of the area of the Lake District. The Iapetus Ocean continued to narrow, but now the subduction zone was on the north side of the ocean. The two continents, Avalonia and Laurentia, got ever closer together.

420 million years ago (middle to late Silurian) – continental collision

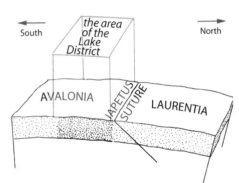

Avalonia and Laurentia collided along a line which we now call the Iapetus Suture. By chance it happens to coincide with the present-day border between England and Scotland (Fig. **L4/2**).

400 million years ago (early Devonian) – rise of the Caledonian mountains

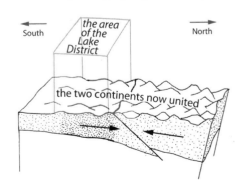

As the process of collision continued, the continental crust shortened and thickened. A huge mountain chain was formed, with its central line in the area which is now the Scottish Highlands. In the Lake District one of the effects of the collision was to produce the cleavage (e.g. Loc. **L23**). The area was also tilted to the south, so that we now see the three main zones of the Lake District – the mudstones, the volcanics, and the shallow-water sediments – in age sequence from north to south.

Erosion of the mountains decreased their height; eventually they were covered by the sea. All the rocks involved in the mountain-building now become the basement for the next sequence of rocks – the Carboniferous – which was deposited unconformably on the up-turned roots of the Caledonian mountains (Loc. **L75**).

A note about the Shap granite, which we shall see on the Walk only from a distance (at Loc. **R2**) or as glacial erratics (at Loc. **R3**): this elegant rock was intruded as a magma 404 million years ago, at the end of the Caledonian mountain-building episode. It must not be confused with the much older Ennerdale granite (452 million years old). To keep things simple, we've omitted the Shap granite from the history we have just related. Its important role in applying numerical dates to the sequence of stratigraphic units (the chart in the Introduction) is part of another story.

INTRODUCTION TO RAVENSTONEDALE AND THE ROCKS OF THE CARBONIFEROUS

Age range: 359-299 million years ago
Latitude: equatorial
Climate: humid tropical

From Shap Abbey to Kirkby Stephen the bedrock is of Carboniferous age. Early in the Carboniferous, the older rocks of the Lake District, much reduced by erosion, formed a low-lying island surrounded by warm shallow tropical seas.

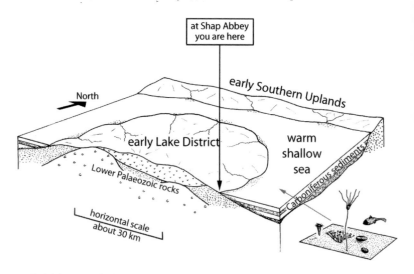

Subsidence of the land, or rise of sea level, allowed Carboniferous sediments to overlap progressively further onto the land area of the Lake District.

We walked over Carboniferous rocks near the west coast, where they were covered by superficial rocks. They are only slightly easier to see here. We shall see enough, however, to be aware that **limestones** form an important part. The area of northern

England was at this time, 360 million years ago, close to the equator, and the seas were clear and warm. This was ideal for organic life, whose dead shells, made of **calcite** (calcium carbonate), form almost the whole of the limestone. The rock differs from other common sediments – sandstones and mudstones – in containing little or no material weathered out of pre-existing rocks.

At the present day, limestone is being deposited in tropical areas like the Bahamas, the Persian Gulf, and coral islands and reefs in the Pacific Ocean. Along with the shelly material of obvious organic origin, fine-grained carbonate sediments form a major part of these environments. The same is true of ancient limestone sediments, which range from richly fossiliferous shell beds and coral-reef limestones to calcite mud. Fossils may appear in almost any kind of limestone, and are most clearly seen when they project from weathered surfaces of the rock. We illustrate here some of the commoner varieties.

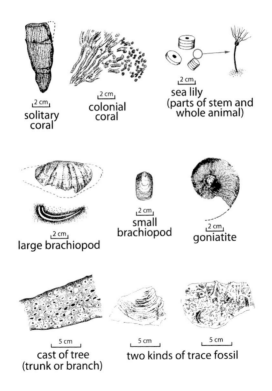

*A selection of Carboniferous fossils. The ones you are most likely to find are colonial or solitary **corals**, stems of **sea lilies**, and large **brachiopods** – all in limestones. Less common are small brachiopods and **goniatites** in mudstones, and **trace fossils** and plant remains in sandstones. Goniatites were ancestors of the **ammonites**. Trace fossils are the trails left by animals moving on or through the sediments – the ancient equivalent of footprints.*

3. RAVENSTONEDALE

We walk on into limestone country of the Carboniferous. Near Kirkby Stephen the Walk crosses over rocks of Permian age, with evidence for another episode of continental collision – but this time far to the south. During the Ice Age the area was covered by a lowland ice sheet.

THE WALK – SHAP TO KIRKBY STEPHEN

From Moss Grove at the south end of Shap village, follow roads and footpaths to a bridge over the railway and then between stone walls and over open fields for 1½ km to a footbridge over the M6 motorway.

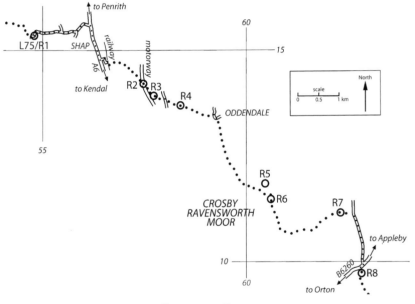

Shap to near Orton.

THE SHAP GRANITE

Loc. **R2**, NY 575 142, the footbridge over the motorway, giving a view to the south, past the lime works.

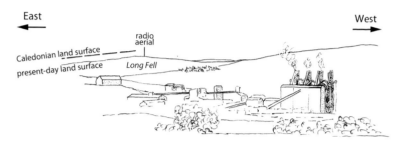

East → West →

radio aerial

Caledonian land surface
present-day land surface   Long Fell

*Fig. **R2**. The bedrock of Long Fell below the distant radio aerial is Shap Granite, outcropping over a total area of about 8 square kilometres.*

The granite was intruded **404** million years ago as liquid **magma** into the surrounding Lower Palaeozoic rocks. Erosion following the Caledonian mountain-building exposed the granite. The 360-million-year-old land surface (the same one as at Shap Abbey) would have been only a few tens of metres above Long Fell.

We shall not see the granite in place, but it will become very familiar as boulders transported by glaciers, starting with the next Location.

The kilns produce very pure lime, for use in steel-making, from a limestone quarry on the hill to your left.

Follow the path parallel to the motorway for a short distance and then bear left across a field covered with boulders and hawthorn bushes.

Loc. **R3**, NY 578 139, in the field east of the motorway. The numerous boulders of Shap Granite were carried by ice from the small outcrop of the granite to the south and deposited in boulder clay when the ice melted. The clay and finer materials have been weathered away, leaving the boulders as **erratics** on the land surface.

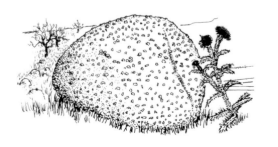

*Fig. **R3**. Shap Granite is an easily recognised rock, distinct from any other British granite. The characteristic feature is the large pink **feldspar** crystals; the rest of the rock is finer pink-grey material.*

118

When first released from the ice the boulders would have been scraped smooth by abrasion in the ice. Their present poxy appearance, with the big feldspar crystals standing proud of the rest of the rock by 2-3 millimetres, is the result of weathering in the last 10,000 years.

Walk on for ¾ km along the path, crossing a minor road. The next Location is beside the path at the south end of a prominent limestone crag.

CALM SEA IN THE CARBONIFEROUS

Loc. **R4**, NY 583 137. Though we have been walking over limestone all the way from Shap Abbey, this is the first exposure of this very common rock-type we have seen on the Walk.

*Fig. **R4/1**. One thick bed of limestone, with traces of layers within it. No fossils are visible to the unaided eye, though a microscope would reveal that the whole rock is made up of organically derived calcite. The irregularly sculptured surface results from the rock being slowly dissolved by rain.*

From the same Location, look back to the west and the Lake District hills.

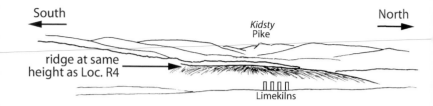

South   Kidsty   North
                                            Pike

ridge at same
height as Loc. R4
                                                              Limekilns

*Fig. **R4/2**. The bedding of the limestones at this Location is near-enough horizontal. To the west the first ridge beyond the limekilns is about at the same height as we are here. The shoreline of the shallow sea that deposited the limestones would have been at the same level. Imagine the green fields replaced by clear blue sea and you have a picture like the scenery of the early Carboniferous. You can see that the higher peaks of the Lake District would have been dry land.*

A modern equivalent of the scene might be the sea between the Great Barrier Reef and the east coast of Australia.

The next Location is 3½ km ahead. Continue on the path, crossing the road to Hardendale Quarry, and then on a stony track to Oddendale. Just before you reach the belt of trees, turn right onto a well-defined path. In 1½ km, shortly after the crest of the slope, bear left towards the corner of an evergreen plantation, and then left again to a low cairn on the next ridge. The cairn is on the indistinct line of a Roman road, and is at the south end of a prominent area of limestone pavement – our next Location.

LIMESTONE SCENERY

All the way from Hardendale we have been walking over typical grass-covered limestone upland with the bedrock appearing patchily as limestone pavement. There is very little surface water, as most of the drainage is underground. Areas of lime-hating plants like heather, bilberry, and coniferous trees indicate places where the limestone is covered by boulder clay or where the local bedrock is sandstone or mudstone.

Loc. **R5**, NY 605 118, 100 metres north of the cairn on the ridge.

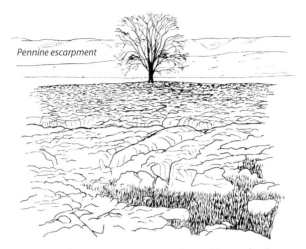

*Fig. **R5**. Limestone pavement, formed by gradual
solution and enlargement of joints.*

The thin soil supports grass and rare lime-loving plants, and in this instance a stately wych elm. In the distance are the Vale of Eden and the escarpment of the Pennines.

Walk on along the path, which bends gradually right (south), for ½ km to a very large round boulder beside the path near the top of the slope leading down to Lyvennet Beck.

SHAP GRANITE (AGAIN)

Loc. **R6**, NY 606 114.

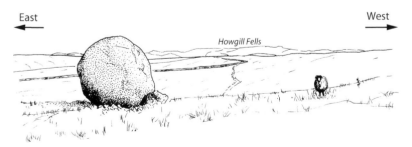

*Fig. **R6**. The erratic boulder of Shap Granite is 2 metres in diameter,
probably weighs about 2 tonnes, and is 4 km from the outcrop of the granite.*

Try to visualise the power of an ice sheet that could move not just this one boulder, but thousands of comparable size, and not just 4 km, but up to 150 km (to Robin Hood's Bay, for instance)!

121

In the distance are the Howgill Fells, a southeasterly continuation of the rocks of the Lake District.

The next Location is 2 km ahead. Walk to the corner of the wall on the opposite side of the valley and then follow the wall for 1 km. Where the wall turns sharply left continue straight ahead across open moor and down to a square walled field.

THE EFFECT OF A RESISTANT LAYER ON THE SCENERY

The next two Locations relate to a thick layer (appropriately called the Great Scar Limestone) of the Carboniferous rocks and the way it influences the scenery. The sediments dip at low angles to slightly east of north. The Great Scar Limestone is more resistant to erosion than the layers below and above it, so it makes a prominent ridge.

Loc. **R7**, NY 623 112, by the square field, or anywhere convenient with a view to the east. The long smooth slope is a **dip slope** of the top of the Great Scar Limestone. The limestone appears patchily as pavement almost buried by grassland.

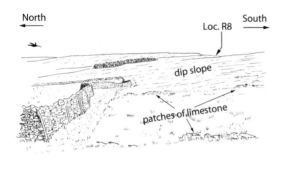

*Fig. **R7/1**. The view southeast from the square field.*

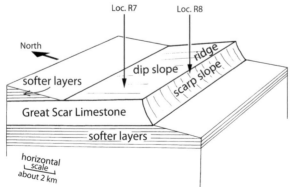

*Fig. **R7/2**. Cartoon showing dip and scarp slopes.*

The next Location is 2 km ahead, just beyond the top of the dip slope. Continue on the path to the tarmac road and follow it to the right, to the crest of the hill and the B6260 road. After the cattle grid a green lane leads downhill to the left. Stop where the field opens out near a ruined lime kiln.

Loc. **R8**, NY 629 098, a disused shallow quarry in limestone.

*Fig. **R8/1**. Well-bedded Carboniferous limestones, dipping gently to the right (north). The environment of deposition here was similar to that of the first limestone we saw.*

*Fig. **R8/2**. From the same Location, looking in the opposite direction, the bedding shows as faint ledges on the hillside. The ridge formed by the top of the Great Scar Limestone is to the left. If the grass could be removed, the scarp slope down to the fields below would expose about 100 metres thickness of successive layers of the Limestone.*

Lime kiln.

The next Location is 2 km further on. If you are walking into Orton go straight on downhill. Otherwise bear left, and in ¾ km turn left on a small tarmac road, first east and then south to Scarside Farm. Shortly after the farm, go left on a path across a field and then to a lane.

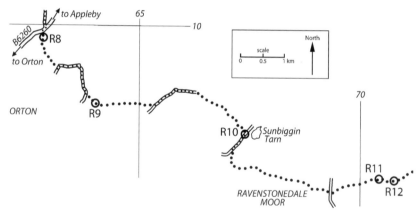

Orton to Ravenstonedale Moor.

SHAP GRANITE IN A STONE CIRCLE

Loc. **R9**, NY 640 082, Gamelands stone circle can be easily viewed from the stile beside the lane.

*Fig. **R9**. All the stones are erratic boulders of Shap Granite – except one; maybe quality control failed on that day 4000 years ago.*

The next Location is 4 km further. The Walk continues along the path at the foot of the scarp slope of the Great Scar Limestone. Turn left on a minor road, go past Sunbiggin Farm, and then on a path across the open moorland. At points where this path is joined by others, each time take the choice to the right. As you arrive at another road there is a view to Sunbiggin Tarn.

A SITE OF SPECIAL SCIENTIFIC INTEREST

Loc. **R10**, NY 674 077, where the path joins the tarmac road.

*Fig. **R10**. Sunbiggin Tarn. Though the bedrock is limestone (where usually most of the drainage is underground), it is here overlain by impermeable boulder clay. The varied soils create differing habitats for plants – the Tarn is an important nature reserve.*

*The next Location is 4½ km ahead. Turn right (southwest) along the road to a small rise, where you take a path to the left. The path curves gently left round the rim of a shallow valley and then into a long dry valley with occasional exposures of limestone, and on to a road. Straight ahead there is another path, and on its right a wall which will be a useful guide to the Route as far as Loc. **R13**.*

A RIVER ENTERS THE CARBONIFEROUS SEA

Loc. **R11**, NY 704 067, at a small steep-sided gully – the guide wall leaps up on the far side.

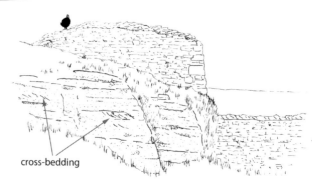

*Fig. **R11**. Red-weathering sandstone, with cross-bedding, on the east side of the gully.*

cross-bedding

The sandstone appears also in small quarries immediately to the left of this drawing. It forms a continuous outcrop for several kilometres (its course can be roughly picked out by areas of heather in this predominantly limestone country). It will be better seen 3 km further on.

THE EFFECT OF A GLACIER ON LOWLAND SCENERY – DRUMLINS

Loc. **R12**, NY 707 067, or anywhere with a view to the south.

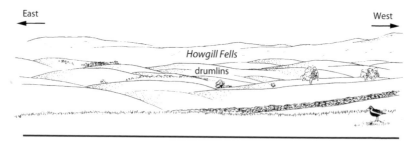

East

West

Howgill Fells

drumlins

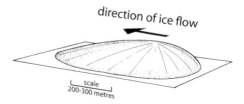

direction of ice flow

scale
200-300 metres

*Fig. **R12**. The low rounded hills are drumlins, deposits from the base of a glacier.*

In this view the ice flowed away from an ice-cap on the Howgill Fells (in the background) and directly towards us. The lower drawing shows the idealised shape of a drumlin.

The very characteristic appearance of an area of drumlins is known as "basket-of-eggs" topography.

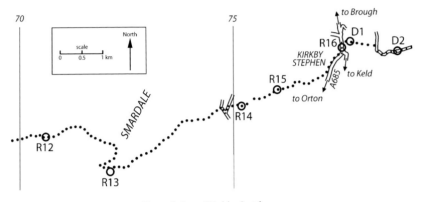

Smardale to Kirkby Stephen.

The next Location is 3 km ahead. Continue along the path for ¾ km, keeping the guide wall to your right. At NY 713 069, where the path enters a small dip and another wall comes in from the left, go through the gate and walk on beside the guide wall. Shortly, cross to the other (south) side of the guide wall and stay close to the wall (to avoid walking over Severals, a nearly invisible but important archaeological site covering the top of the low hill to the south). The wall leads steeply down to Smardale Bridge in the valley of Scandal Beck. On the final descent well-bedded fossiliferous limestones are exposed on the hillside.

Smardale Bridge.

127

SANDSTONE AMONG THE LIMESTONES

Loc. **R13**, NY 721 059, a small quarry beside the stream 100 metres south of Smardale Bridge.

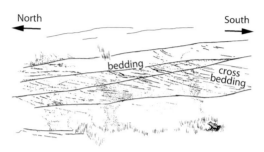

*Fig. **R13**. Red Carboniferous sandstones dipping gently to the north. The cross-bedding dips to the south, indicating a northerly source (the eroding Caledonian mountains in Scotland) for the streams and the sediment they carried. The red colour implies a hot arid environment – remember that we are at this time close to the equator.*

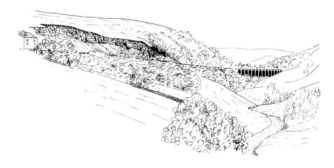

Scandal Beck, Smardalegill Viaduct, and limestone quarries. The rock is the Great Scar Limestone, which was used for building stone and for making lime.

From Smardale Bridge the Walk climbs the scarp slope of the Great Scar Limestone, followed by a long descent of the dip slope nearly to Kirkby Stephen.

The next Location is 4 km further on. Stay on the track from Smardale Bridge, leading up to Smardale Fell. Keep the wall on your left. In the wide dry valley where the wall bends left, go straight on up the further hillside. Soon the wall returns – follow it down to a road, where you turn right. At the road junction in 300 metres turn left, and after ¼ km go right onto a field path. The path passes between drumlins and past faint ridges that mark the remains of walls of a prehistoric settlement.

A CLOSER VIEW OF DRUMLINS

Loc. **R14**, NY 752 073, in the field between the road and the railway bridge.

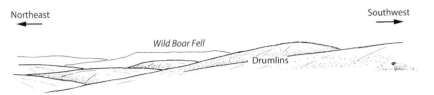

Northeast   Southwest

Wild Boar Fell

Drumlins

*Fig. **R14**. The low rounded hillocks are drumlins. The limestone bedrock is exposed in a field to the left of the path.*

Continue on the path to the bridge under the Settle-to-Carlisle railway. On the far side the path passes the site of another prehistoric settlement. Walk on into a valley between two drumlins.

The rough ground marks an ancient settlement.

Loc. **R15**, NY 760 077, shallow scrapes into the top surface of the drumlin on the left of the path.

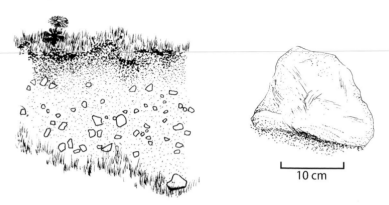

Fig. R15. Left: red boulder clay deposited by a melting ice sheet about 10,000 years ago. The present-day soil profile blends downwards into the boulder clay. Right: a small loose boulder, showing scratches made by abrasion with other rock materials during transport in the ice.

Walk on into Kirkby Stephen (2 km) – follow the path down to Greenriggs Farm, where you turn left and use the track and road into the town.

At Greenriggs Farm the bedrock changes from marine limestones (330 million years old), in the lower part of the Carboniferous, to desert sandstones (270 million years old) of the next younger stratigraphic system, the Permian. There is nothing on the ground to provide evidence of the change, or the reason for the big gap in the sequence of rocks, let alone the events which brought them about. These are described in the Journal.

THE BUILDING STONES OF KIRKBY STEPHEN

Loc. **R16**, NY 775 086, anywhere in Kirkby Stephen where you can see red or pink building stone.

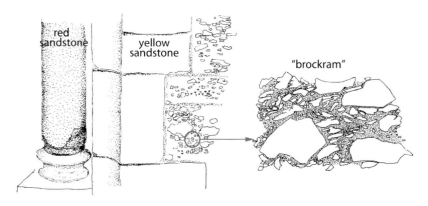

*Fig. **R16**. Three different building stones in the doorway of a former church, now The Emporium. The properties of the various stones, such as colour and the ease of cutting or carving, determine how they are used in building.*

The red column is desert sandstone from the local New Red Sandstone (a name for the combined Permian and Triassic – the Permo-Triassic – and similar to the coastal rocks at St Bees Head). The pale yellow sandstone in the sides of the doorway is from the Carboniferous. The pink-grey stone of the wall (the inset gives more detail) is a very distinctive rock of Permian age, but made of angular pieces of Carboniferous limestone. It has the local name brockram, and comes from disused quarries south of the town. The Journal explains its significance.

JOURNAL 6 – KIRKBY STEPHEN

THE CARBONIFEROUS ROCKS IN RAVENSTONEDALE

You probably got a rather simple view of the rocks of Ravenstonedale because for most of the way we walked on the dip slope, or at the base of the scarp slope, of one prominent layer of limestone. By contrast with the violent history of the Lower Palaeozoic rocks of the Lake District, the environment of deposition of the Great Scar Limestone was a peaceful shallow-marine interlude.

The sandstone at Smardale Bridge makes a sharp contrast with the limestones above and below. It is one exposure of a layer which is continuous within the Carboniferous for more than 20 km. The sandstones are a reminder that erosion of the ageing Caledonian mountains to the north was still proceeding.

For the final 2 km of the Walk the bedrock was Permo-Triassic desert sandstones and the brockram, unseen except in the local building stones.

WHAT YOU DON'T SEE IN KIRKBY STEPHEN, AND WHY IT'S IMPORTANT

If we were to draw a small-scale map of Britain with lines to indicate significant geological and geographical boundaries, three of them would converge on the Kirkby Stephen area:

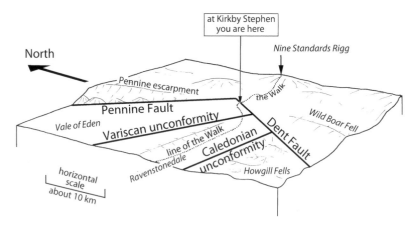

Map of the Kirkby Stephen area as an oblique view.

To help the explanation we extend the map downwards:

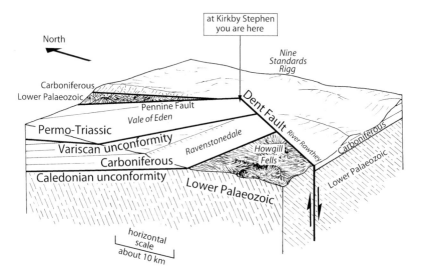

Cartoon of the Kirkby Stephen area, showing the three geological boundaries and their continuation below ground:

- *The Caledonian unconformity between the Lower Palaeozoic of the Howgill Fells and the Carboniferous of Ravenstonedale. This is the same ancient land surface that we saw at Shap Abbey.*

- *The Variscan unconformity between the Carboniferous and the Permo-Triassic (read on for more detail).*

- *The Dent-Pennine Fault System (explained below). This cuts across the east end of the Howgill Fells and also produces the Pennine escarpment.*

Although on the route of the Walk you are able to see only sketchy evidence for any of the boundaries, we could not allow you to walk straight over them without comment. (Why is that, if we can't see anything? Answer – because they represent major episodes in the geological evolution of Britain, and to leave them out would be like writing a history of Britain without 1066 and all that.)

THE VARISCAN UNCONFORMITY

The bedrock of the area around Kirkby Stephen is the Permo-Triassic. The Permian brockram (Fig. **R16**), with its angular pieces of Carboniferous limestone, is clear evidence of an **unconformity** – deformation and uplift of the Carboniferous rocks exposed them to erosion, and at the same time the brockram was being deposited on the new land surface. Earth movements that brought about this relationship were a distant effect of a continental collision and mountain-building that affected southern Britain, 400 km away to the south. The collision, named the Variscan, 300 million years ago, was between a northern Laurasian continent and a southern Gondwana continent.

THE DENT FAULT

The Dent Fault (named after the village 20 km south of Kirkby Stephen, not the hill you climbed near the beginning of the Walk) is one segment of a major **fault** system that forms the western boundary of the whole length of the Pennines. Part of its movement was a result of the Variscan deformation.

The only fault we have seen so far is the pocket-sized example at Loc. **L33**, which we were able to examine in detail (Journal **4**). The Dent Fault is one of the biggest in England, but its sheer scale makes it difficult to see. It does, however, have a dramatic effect on the scenery. The deep valley of the River Rawthey 7 km southwest of Kirkby Stephen is eroding the weakened rocks along the line of the fault. On the west side of the valley are the rounded hills of Lower Palaeozoic rocks in the Howgill Fells. On the east side are the scarp slopes of nearly horizontal layers of Carboniferous rocks that make Wild Boar Fell.

We can estimate how big the fault is from its vertical **displacement** – the difference in the levels of the rocks each side of the fault plane. We saw in the unconformity at Shap Abbey that the Carboniferous rocks cover the Lower Palaeozoic; in the same way Carboniferous rocks originally lay across the Howgill Fells but have now been eroded away. So we can say that the amount of vertical movement of the fault is at least the height of the Howgill Fells – 500 metres above the River Rawthey. Detailed mapping shows that it is more like 1000 metres.

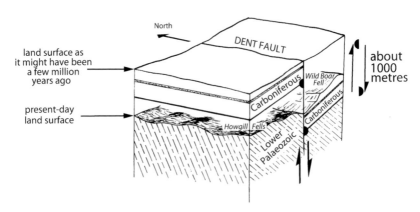

A composite cartoon to show how the Carboniferous rocks originally extended over the Howgill Fells, and the amount of displacement of the Dent Fault.

The Pennine Fault (the northern continuation of the Dent Fault) is even bigger, bringing Lower Palaeozoic rocks into contact with Permo-Triassic – a vertical displacement of 1500 metres or more. These are by any measure big faults – for comparison, the faults that define the East African Rift Valley have a vertical displacement of only a few thousand metres. It so happens that at Kirkby Stephen the fault system has a very small displacement and, moreover, is partly covered by the Permo-Triassic, so that one could walk across it almost without noticing. Even so, it is still able to make its presence felt – there was a small earthquake in Kirkby Stephen in 1970.

OTHER BIG FAULTS IN NORTHERN ENGLAND

We need now to think about rocks on a very big scale – in fact, most of northern England. To simplify the situation, picture the **basement** at the end of the Caledonian mountain-building as forming a vast rigid slab about 30 km thick and at least 200 km across. (That is, the thickness of the continental crust, and the width of the country from coast to coast.) For convenience, think of the top surface of the slab as flat (and on the scale we are thinking of that is near-enough true).

After the mountain-building and before the start of the Carboniferous the basement slab was broken by faults – about half a dozen major ones. From this time on, the pieces of the slab, referred to as blocks and troughs, were able to respond independently to movements deep down in the crust.

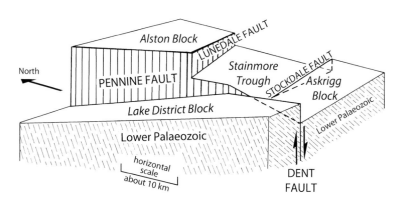

The deep structure of part of northern England. This is the same as the cartoon of the Kirkby Stephen area, with the Permo-Triassic and Carboniferous rocks stripped off to reveal the top surface of the Lower Palaeozoic (the basement).

THE SCENERY OF BLOCKS AND TROUGHS

Present-day erosion has smoothed the boundaries between the blocks and troughs, but each area still has its own distinctive scenery:

The tilted Lake District Block has three types of scenery. These are the Lower Palaeozoic mountains of the Lake District and the Howgill Fells, the Carboniferous scarp-and-dip slopes and grazing country that we saw in Ravenstonedale, and the nearly flat topography and fertile soils of the Permo-Triassic around Kirkby Stephen and in the Vale of Eden.

On the east side of the Dent Fault the broad valley of lower Teesdale roughly coincides with the Stainmore Trough, while the narrower dales of the Swale and the Wear are in the Askrigg and Alston Blocks. The A66 trunk road from Scotch Corner to Penrith uses the Stainmore Trough in preference to the more challenging terrain of the adjacent blocks.

For an amphibian early in the Carboniferous or for a reptile in the Permian the large-scale scenery would have been recognisably similar to that of the present day. The Lake District, the Howgills, and the Pennines would all have been upland areas, with shallow sea or lowland desert between. And no doubt animals of the time would have felt the effects of earthquakes that marked successive movements of the faults.

INTRODUCTION TO THE CARBONIFEROUS ROCKS OF THE YORKSHIRE DALES

There is still another 3 or 4 km of the Walk before we are completely clear of the effects of the Dent Fault. We then cross from the Lake District Block to the Stainmore Trough, with a steady climb up Nine Standards Rigg, and through 600 metres thickness of Carboniferous sediments.

The gently dipping Carboniferous bedrock is not particularly well exposed, but the resistant limestone and sandstone layers make distinct crags and ledges on hill-slopes, often showing better from a distance than when one is standing on them. (This terracing is also the reason why there always seems to be just one more ridge to climb before reaching the top of a hill.)

The Walk east of the Dent Fault starts on the Great Scar Limestone, near the base of the Carboniferous. From the Great Scar Limestone to the top of Nine Standards Rigg we cross over twelve more limestones, and a similar number of sandstones and mudstones. The limestones and sandstones were all formed close to sea level – just below or just above. Two questions arise:

- How is it possible for a considerable thickness of sediment to have been made all at or near sea level?

- How are the same kinds of sediment repeated so often?

These will be questions to ponder as we continue the Walk. We shall try to answer them after we have seen some of the rocks on the ground.

One of the limestones, half-way up Nine Standards Rigg, known as the Main Limestone, will keep us company all the way to Richmond. It is 300 metres higher in the sequence and 25 million years younger than the Great Scar Limestone. We shall see it so often that one could get the impression that it is the only unit of any significance in this part of the Carboniferous. In fact, it is just one particularly widespread unit which is often better exposed than other layers.

The kinds of fossil that you may find in the Carboniferous rocks of the Dales are the same as those shown in Journal **5**.

Mineral veins are prominent in the rocks of the Dales and were a major part of the economy of the area from Roman times up to the end of the nineteenth century. We shall see the evidence of the mines and mining when we get into Swaledale.

4. THE YORKSHIRE DALES

After crossing the Dent-Pennine Fault and seeing its dramatic effect on the scenery of northern England, we continue on Carboniferous rocks, more varied than those we saw in Ravenstonedale, and giving us a wider view of the Carboniferous environment.

THE WALK – KIRKBY STEPHEN TO KELD

From the marketplace in Kirkby Stephen walk down the narrow lane towards the river and cross it by Frank's Bridge. The next Location is 10 metres beyond the bridge.

A CLOSER LOOK AT SHAP GRANITE

Loc. **D1**, NY 777 087, the memorial stone beside the path on the east side of Frank's Bridge.

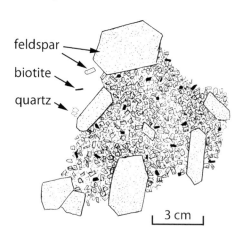

feldspar

biotite

quartz

*Fig. **D1**. The polished top of the boulder reveals the fine structure of the Shap Granite.*

3 cm

You are probably familiar with the large pink crystals of feldspar, prominent on the weathered surfaces of the erratic boulders we have seen several times. The finer parts of the rock are colourless transparent quartz (usually looking grey), feldspar (pink or white), and black **mica**. All the crystals in the rock are locked firmly together – a characteristic feature of an igneous rock made by solidification of a liquid. This also explains why the rock survives being transported in ice, and why it makes a durable ornamental stone for buildings. Rock from the Shap granite quarry is used, for example, in the Albert Memorial in London and in St Mary's Cathedral in Edinburgh.

Try to imagine this rock as it would have looked when it was a liquid at 600-700°C (bright-red heat), rather viscous, with the larger feldspar crystals representing the first parts of the magma to solidify.

The next Location is 1¼ km ahead. Walk on along the path and then across a field, aiming for the far-left corner, where a walled track leads into Hartley village. The houses here provide a final view of the pink-red building stones of the Permo-Triassic. Turn right when you reach the road. In 300 metres, where the road goes straight ahead into a large quarry, turn uphill to the left, and stop for a moment when you are clear of the trees.

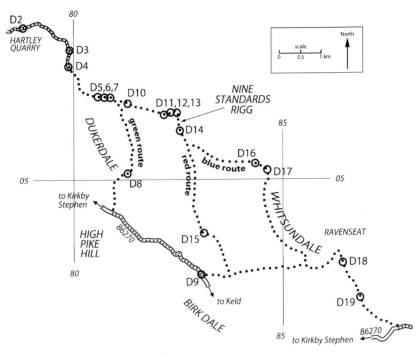

Hartley to Ravenseat.

Loc. **D2**, NY 787 085. This is about as close as we can get to the Variscan **unconformity**. The rocks in the quarry are low down in the Carboniferous, about 330 million years old, all the rest of the Carboniferous having been removed by erosion about 300 million years ago. The Permo-Triassic sandstones which spread across the ancient land surface are marked by the sandy soil and evergreen trees beside the road. From here on, the bedrock is Carboniferous, which continues without interruption as far as Richmond, 52 km ahead.

Stop anywhere in the next ½ km where you get a view of the Pennine escarpment to the left (north) and to the right into the big quarry.

THE GREAT SCAR LIMESTONE

Hartley quarry is in the Great Scar Limestone of the Carboniferous.

Fig. D2/1. The total thickness of the limestone is several hundred metres – much greater than the depth of the quarry. The clear warm shallow sea conditions persisted here for many thousands of years.

The rock was initially quarried to make pure lime for the steel industry and for agriculture. Now it's mainly used for aggregate and road-stone.

VIEW TO THE PENNINE ESCARPMENT

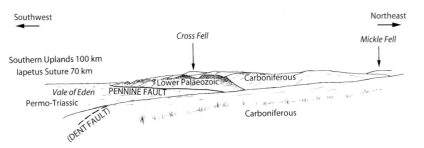

Fig. D2/2. The view looking north from near Hartley quarry. The Pennine Fault runs through the low ground at the foot of the escarpment (and continues as the Dent Fault in the ground to the left of our viewpoint). If the air is exceptionally clear you might be able to see the hills of the Southern Uplands of Scotland, on the far side of the Iapetus Suture (compare with Fig. I4/2).

139

The central part of the view is shown in the cartoon below, with the three important boundaries – the Caledonian and Variscan unconformities and the Pennine Fault. Scenically, from west to east, the Permo-Triassic forms the low ground of the Vale of Eden, separated by the Pennine Fault from the rounded hills of Lower Palaeozoic rocks; the Carboniferous makes the main escarpment and the high plateau to the east.

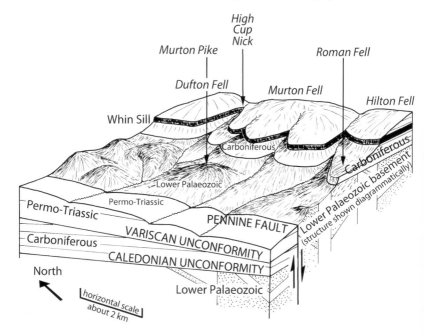

Fig. D2/3. Cartoon of a small part of the Pennine escarpment. The Whin Sill is an intrusion of dolerite making a prominent line of crags. We don't cross the Sill on the line of the Walk but it's worth mentioning as a significant feature of the rocks and scenery of northern England.

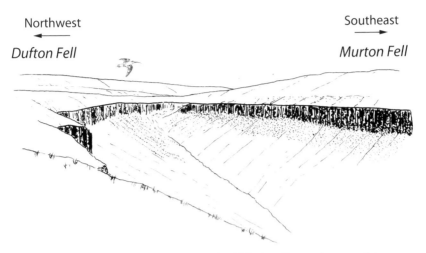

Northwest ← **Dufton Fell**

Southeast → **Murton Fell**

The Whin Sill, with its prominent vertical jointing, frames the upper slopes of High Cup Nick. This huge dolerite intrusion, with an estimated volume of at least 200 cubic kilometres, extends below most of the north Pennines. It probably represents a hot spot (Journal 4) below the area of northern England 300 million years ago

Continue on the road for another 1¼ km.

FINAL VIEWS OF THE DENT FAULT SYSTEM

Loc. **D3**, NY 799 080, where the road makes a double bend at the bridge across a small stream. Here we cross the most easterly fault of the Dent Fault System.

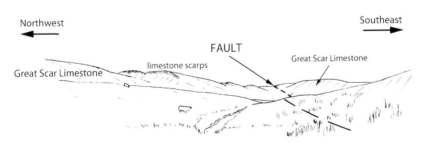

Northwest ←

Southeast →

FAULT

limestone scarps

Great Scar Limestone

Great Scar Limestone

*Fig. **D3/1**. Birkett Beck, looking northeast.*

The valley follows the course of the fault, or more likely the disturbed and weakened rocks adjacent to the fault. The fault itself is not exposed but its outcrop can be mapped along the lowest slopes of the hill on the right of the stream. The Great Scar

141

Limestone appears twice in the view because its outcrop is repeated by the fault. The small scarps on the left of the fault are formed by a thin limestone younger than the Great Scar Limestone.

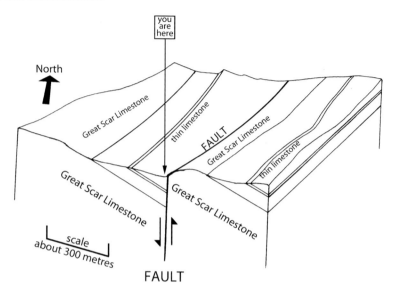

Fig. D3/2. Cartoon of the same area as the drawing, to show how the fault continues below ground.

Walk on up the road for ½ km.

Loc. **D4**, NY 798 076, anywhere with a view to the southwest.

*Fig. **D4**. We are standing here on the line of the same fault as at the last Location, but looking in the opposite direction. The fault continues southwards, approximately on the line of the bushes, and passes to the left of Birkett Hill. The hill is made of Great Scar Limestone dipping steeply towards us. In the far distance, behind Birkett Hill, the fault (actually the Dent Fault System as a whole) runs between the Howgill Fells (Lower Palaeozoic) and Wild Boar Fell (Carboniferous).*

That is the last we shall see of the Dent Fault System and its complications. We are now into the Stainmore Trough. It may not feel much of a trough as we climb to the top of Nine Standards Rigg, but remember that the Trough is a much bigger and older structure than individual hills and vales. The Walk will take us in ascending order through a considerable thickness of Carboniferous sediments.

Walk on to the end of the tarmac road and take the track through the gate to the left. The next Location is by the barn 1 km ahead.

THE ROCKS OF THE CARBONIFEROUS

In the next ½ km of the Walk we shall see exposures of the three kinds of sediment that make nearly all of this part of the Carboniferous.

Loc. **D5**, NY 806 069. A low ridge of white sandstone on the north side of the path, opposite the barn and sheepfold.

*Fig. **D5/1**. The sandstone (below the tumble of loose boulders) dips at 20° to the east (right). The whole thickness of the unit is about 10 metres.*

Cross-bedding in some of the beds shows that the sandstones were deposited from quickly flowing water, suggesting a river environment. This persisted for a considerable time, as shown by the thickness of the unit as a whole.

Take a look at Dukerdale, to the south of the path.

143

Northeast ← → Southwest

*Fig. **D5/2**. Dukerdale from the north.*

The Main Limestone, about 20 metres thick, makes the crags high on the valley sides.

Walk on for 300 metres.

Loc. **D6**, NY 807 069, where Reigill crosses the path.

*Fig. **D6**. An exposure of dark grey mudstones with thin silty layers. The thickness of this unit is at least 5 metres.*

Guessing at a typical rate of deposition of at most a millimetre per year, this muddy environment lasted for several thousands of years. The small number of silty layers and the absence of sands suggest that the muds were deposited in coastal or marine conditions – close enough to land for mud and some silt to be carried from rivers into the sea, but well away from a river estuary or shoreline where the sand would have been deposited.

Walk on for 200 metres to the bend in the path at the top of the small rise you can see from Loc. D6.

Loc. **D7**, NY 809 069, an exposure of bedrock in Reigill, to the left of the path.

*Fig. **D7**. The limestone is about 10 metres thick.*

Here the environment was clear warm shallow sea, with no input of sand or mud from any nearby land. Again, the environment was stable for a long time.

As we continue up Nine Standards Rigg, we walk over more limestones, mudstones, and sandstones like the ones we have just seen (though most of them are poorly exposed). (Remember that one of the questions posed earlier was why the same kinds of sediment should be repeated in this way.)

Continue for 200 metres to the signpost (NY 810 067) at the junction of the paths. From here there are three routes, planned so as to spread the wear on the paths, to cross Nine Standards Rigg. All three of the routes include big stretches of boggy ground and places where it is unclear what direction to take. The safest route in bad weather is the Green Route. The Red and Blue Routes go to the top of Nine Standards Rigg and separate a little south of the summit. All three routes join again near Ravenseat in Whitsundale. The rocks and scenery are similar on all three routes.

- Green Route – east side of Dukerdale; December to April. Lower slopes of Nine Standards Rigg, limestone pavement, swallow holes.

- Red Route – to Nine Standards Rigg summit, then south; May to July. Upland erosion, views from the summit.

- Blue Route – to Nine Standards Rigg, then east; August to November. Upland erosion, views from the summit, river patterns in Upper Whitsundale.

DUKERDALE TO RAVENSEAT – THE GREEN ROUTE

*From the junction of the paths at NY 810 067 take the path to the right, keeping the wall on your right, and along the top of the Main Limestone in Fig. **D5/2**. Numerous swallow holes mark the position of the limestone. The next Location is at the head of Dukerdale, 2 km from where you leave the Red/Blue Routes.*

Loc. **D8**, NY 813 051, with a view down Dukerdale.

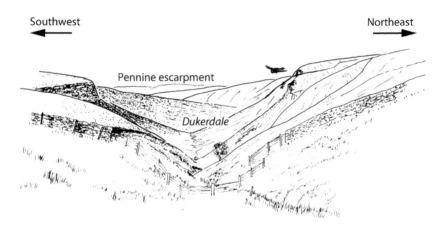

*Fig. **D8/1**. The Main Limestone makes the crags on each side of the dale.*

146

It is not clear what has guided the formation of the valley. It does not have the classic **U**-shape to suggest that it was carved by a glacier, though it would certainly have been filled with ice. The topography at its top end does not suggest that it is the overflow channel from a glacial lake. There is no fault along the valley to suggest a line of weakness, though its direction is suggestively parallel with the Pennine Fault. Whatever the underlying reasons, it's still a handsome piece of scenery.

At the same Location there is a particularly deep swallow hole in the Main Limestone.

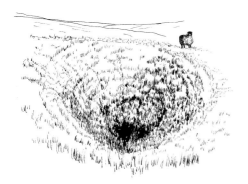

*Fig. **D8/2**. The swallow hole is about 5 metres deep. Sometimes these solution holes in limestone lead to cave systems below.*

Head southwest for ½ km (in the direction of High Pike Hill 3 km away) until you meet a good track leading south to the B6270 road – in total 1 km from the head of Dukerdale. Part of the way crosses a limestone pavement – the Main Limestone again.

The top of the road, ½ km to your right, is the watershed between streams which join the River Eden to drain northwest to the Solway Firth and the Irish Sea and the River Swale flowing east to the Humber estuary and the North Sea. You could say you are standing on the backbone of northern England.

Turn left on the road and stay on it to the next Location in 2¾ km. The wide expanse of moorland to your right is Birkdale.

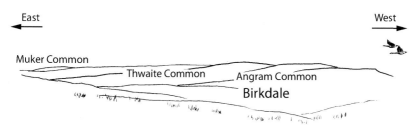

Birkdale, containing the headwaters of the River Swale.

ANOTHER THICK MUDSTONE

Loc. **D9**, NY 831 028, where the road makes a sharp bend to cross Rowantree Gill.

*Fig. **D9**. An exposure of a thick sequence of black mudstones with occasional siltstone layers. This is another of the mudstone layers like the one we saw earlier, but in this instance much thicker.*

*Walk on for 100 metres along the road, then turn left up a well-made track. At the highest point on the track the Red Route comes in from the left. Stay on the track for 3 km to Ravenseat. Loc. **D18**, beyond Ravenseat, is our next scheduled stop.*

DUKERDALE TO RAVENSEAT – THE RED AND BLUE ROUTES

From the junction of the paths at NY 810 067 take the left fork to the top of Nine Standards Rigg (1½ km). The bedrock is patchily exposed, but you will see big exposures of limestones, mudstones, and sandstones in the deeply eroded valley of Faraday Gill to the left of the path. (The stream is named after the family of the great Victorian scientist.)

FEATURES OF UPLAND EROSION

The next three Locations look at effects of erosion on the higher slopes of Nine Standards Rigg.

Loc. **D10**, 813 067, at an elegant stone pillar beside the path.

*Fig. **D10**. A dry gully ends in a swallow hole with low crags of the Main Limestone. The overlapping spurs higher up the gully show that it has been eroded by a stream.*

Loc. **D11**, NY 821 065, where the path shows severe erosion.

*Fig. **D11**. Rapid erosion has undermined timber steps in the path, to a depth of half a metre below the adjacent grass-covered slopes. The new path on the left is already showing signs of erosion.*

Loc. **D12**, NY 822 065, or anywhere with a view of the stream systems on the upper slopes of Nine Standards Rigg.

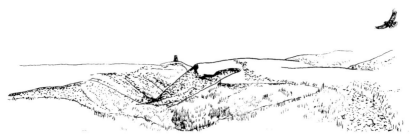

*Fig. **D12**. One of the many gullies, dry or with very small streams, that drain the upper slopes of Nine Standards Rigg. The tops of the gully sides are marked by a well-defined lip where the turf is more resistant to erosion than the underlying mudstone.*

More about this in the Journal at Keld.

Continue along the path to the Nine Standards – about ½ km.

THE NINE STANDARDS AND THE WATERSHED OF NORTHERN ENGLAND

Loc. **D13**, NY 825 066, at the top of Nine Standards Rigg. You are here standing on the watershed of northern England, between streams draining west to the Irish Sea and those flowing east to the North Sea.

*Fig. **D13**. Three of the Nine Standards, and in the foreground part of a mini-quarry which provided the sandstone flags to make the standards. This type of flaggy sandstone is widely used in the Dales as "stone slates".*

"Slate" here is a stonemason's term. The rock is sedimentary, not metamorphosed. It splits easily because there are occasional bedding planes with flakes of colourless **mica** along with the sand grains. (The mica is most likely to have come from erosion of metamorphic rocks in the Scottish Highlands.) This very attractive roofing stone adds its distinctive character to the buildings of the Dales.

The Red and Blue Routes now turn south, past the viewpoint indicator and then the trig. point. On a fine day there are good views in all directions, especially to the west, where you can look back over three chapters of the Walk.

VIEWS FROM THE TOP OF NINE STANDARDS RIGG

Loc. **D14**, NY 825 061, the summit of Nine Standards Rigg.

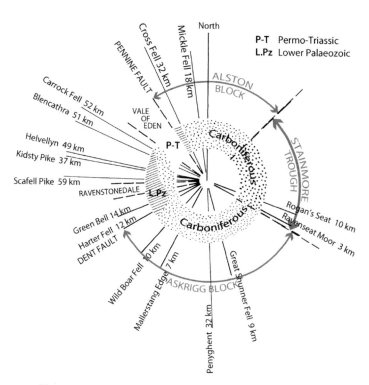

Fig. D14. The panorama from the summit of Nine Standards Rigg, with distances to some of the peaks that may be visible.

To summarise briefly, working clockwise from the southwest: Lower Palaeozoic rocks fill the horizon from Harter Fell through the mountains of central Lake District to Carrock Fell in the northwest. In Ravenstonedale the Lower Palaeozoic is covered by the sediments of the Carboniferous, which in turn are covered by the Permo-Triassic in the Vale of Eden. The Pennine Fault brings a narrow slice of Lower Palaeozoic rocks back to the surface in the Pennine escarpment. The Carboniferous then fills the view all the way round to the southwest, where it is terminated by the Dent Fault.

The block-and-trough structure (Journal **6**) has a distinct, if subtle, effect on the scenery within the Carboniferous. The higher hills of the Pennine escarpment and Mickle Fell are in the Alston Block. The uplands from the southeast to the southwest, with peaks like Great Shunner Fell and Wild Boar Fell and, far to the south, Penyghent are in the Askrigg Block. Between them is the broad expanse of the Stainmore Trough, making slightly lower ground (and you may just be able to pick out the traffic on the A66 trunk road, which uses this easier topography to cross the Pennines).

And that is the final view of the Lake District. Until your next visit!

The Red and Blue Routes continue for ½ km to the SSE and separate at a signpost in an expanse of peaty bog. We continue with the Red Route to where it rejoins the Green Route, and then come back to pick up the Blue Route.

NINE STANDARDS RIGG TO RAVENSEAT – THE RED ROUTE

Head south towards a rough pile of stones (part of an exposure of a thick sandstone that outcrops as a dip slope for a kilometre of the Route, and allows slightly less muddy progress), and then look ahead for a stone pillar on the crest of the ridge. The distance from the trig. point is 2½ km.

Loc. **D15**, NY 831 038.

*Fig. **D15**. The stone pillar standing on the sandstone bedrock from which it was built. The thicker bedding makes for a different style of stonework from that of the Nine Standards.*

Walk SSE down the long slope for a further kilometre. On the way glance to your right to see the wide expanse of Birkdale and the headwaters of the River Swale. At a good track turn left, joining the Green Route to Ravenseat – 3 km further. As you approach Ravenseat and the bridge across Whitsundale Beck you can look left (upstream) to note the flat-bottomed valley, which is referred to at the next Location (D18).

WHITSUNDALE – THE BLUE ROUTE

From the signpost on Nine Standards Rigg head east on an indistinct path marked with occasional posts. As you descend the slope Whitsundale comes into view:

Loc. **D16**, NY 844 054 or thereabouts.

North

South

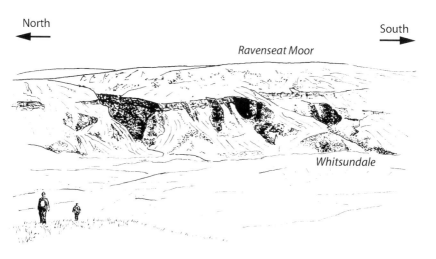

Ravenseat Moor

Whitsundale

*Fig. **D16**. Upper Whitsundale from the west. The dale runs down to the south (right). Gullies in various stages of development cut into the east side of the valley. The crags are made by a sandstone layer.*

Walk on into Whitsundale (½ km). Then follow the path down the right side of the valley.

A MEANDERING STREAM

Loc. **D17**, extending from NY 847 052, where the Walk joins the valley, to NY 855 033, near the south end.

*Fig. **D17/1.** Upper Whitsundale from the north. As you walk on you can see several of the devices a stream uses to take the course of least resistance to its flow.*

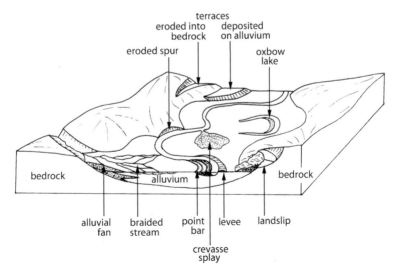

*Fig. **D17/2.** Some features of a river system for comparison with those in Whitsundale. Both erosional and depositional processes are at work.*

Walk on to Ravenseat (4 km from where we joined the top end of Whitsundale).

THE GREEN, RED, AND BLUE ROUTES UNITE AT RAVENSEAT

Walk on, using the path on the left side of the stream. The next Location is in 300 metres.

MORE FEATURES OF RIVER DEVELOPMENT

Loc. **D18**, NY 864 031, beside a waterfall on the right, largely hidden by trees. The reason for the flat valley of the upper part of Whitsundale becomes clear, as a thick resistant sandstone outcrops here, making the waterfall and defining the base level upstream. The sandstone makes a gorge as far as the next Location, where the lower part of the dale opens out again.

Loc. **D19**, NY 868 023, Oven Mouth (an appropriate name for a dramatic scene).

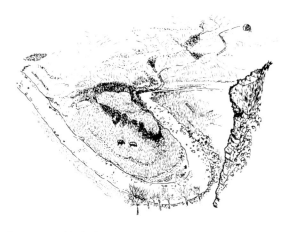

*Fig. **D19**. Whitsundale Beck flows in the gorge of the thick sandstone that makes the cliff on the right.*

It seems unlikely that the river has eroded the incised meander all the way down from where we are standing, but it was certainly at one time level with the promontory of sandstone on the inside of the curve.

Continue on the path till it joins a track just before Low Bridge across the River Swale. Turn left on the road for ½ km, then through a gate to the riverside (total 2 km from Oven Mouth).

155

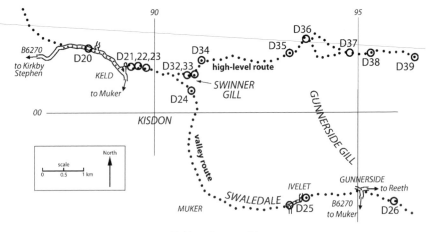

Keld to Gunnerside.

A PICTURESQUE INTERLUDE, WITH OBSERVATIONS TO BE DEVELOPED LATER

Loc. **D20**, NY 884 016, Wain Wath Falls.

*Fig. **D20**. The River Swale at Wain Wath Falls.*

The cliff at the top of the valley side is the Main Limestone. The limestone that makes the falls is the one below the Main Limestone – the same one as at Loc. **D7**. Between the two limestones are softer mudstones, covered by the bushes.

THE NORTH SWALEDALE MINERAL BELT

At the same Location, take a look at the south side of the valley (behind you in Fig. **D20**); there are no matching cliffs or crags to indicate the presence of the limestones. A fault – part of what we shall see later as the North Swaledale Mineral Belt – outcrops along the line of the valley and on the south side displaces the limestones downwards to below ground level.

The valley was present before the Ice Age and was deepened by a glacier. We say more about this in the Journal.

JOURNAL 7 – KELD

A cottage in Keld.

EROSION OF THE HIGHER SLOPES OF NINE STANDARDS RIGG (Locs *D10-12, 16*, and *17*)

The bedrock is poorly exposed on Nine Standards Rigg. Paradoxically, where the bedrock is extensively exposed it is often the softer mudstones rather than the more resistant sandstones and limestones. An explanation seems necessary, and we have seen clues in our Walk.

The vegetation of the higher slopes, much of it mat-grass (an appropriate name in the context) is very effective at binding the thin soil so as to resist erosion. But once the grass layer has been breached, naturally or by the tread of boots, erosion to form a new gully is rapid, and particularly so if the underlying bedrock is mudstone. A stream gets established in the new gully and adjacent gullies become disused. If grass is able to grow on the sides of the new gully, the rate of erosion is slowed, and the vigorous erosion is transferred to another site. This may explain why there are so many small, and often dry, gullies. It is only those that do not get stabilised by the regrowth of vegetation, like Faraday Gill, that turn into bigger streams with extensive exposures of bedrock.

THE CARBONIFEROUS SEDIMENTS (Locs *D5-7, 20*)

We posed two questions about the Carboniferous sediments in the last issue of the Journal; it's now time to answer them.

Most of the sediments were deposited on low-lying land or in shallow sea – close to sea level, and yet at least 600 metres thick. The explanation is that the surface the sediments were deposited on was continuously subsiding. This was most likely because the crust of the Earth was slowly cooling and contracting after the heating effects of the Caledonian mountain-building – remember that rocks like those of the Lake District form the basement below northern England.

The repetition of different types of sediment needs more detailed explanation.

The geography of northern Britain 340 million years ago was dominated by the Caledonian mountains in the north. Rivers carried huge amounts of eroded material from the mountains across a wide floodplain and into a shallow sea to the south. The sediments occur repeatedly in the (upwards) sequence: limestone, mudstone, sandstone. The pattern is distinctive enough to merit a name – **Yoredale cycles** (from an old name for the River Ure in Wensleydale).

(Strictly speaking, we should use the term "cyclothem" for the rocks and **cycle** for the process that makes them. But let's avoid the technical terms.)

The Mississippi **delta** in the Gulf of Mexico is in a similar present-day situation to that of northern England during the Carboniferous. The Mississippi River and its **distributaries** (see the map below) carry vast amounts of sediment. As the distributary channels grow longer they eventually become blocked by their own deposits of sand. New channels then break out to find shorter routes to the sea.

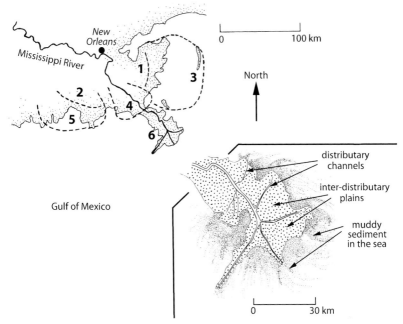

Map of the Gulf Coast of America, showing the Mississippi River and a few of the successive positions of its delta over several thousand years (1 – oldest; 6 – present-day). The inset shows more detail for the present-day delta, including the patterns of dispersal of the finer sediment into the Gulf of Mexico.

The inter-distributary floodplains consist of fresh-water silts and muds deposited when the river overflows, along with marine and brackish-water muds, and marshy vegetation. Marine sediments are deposited in the Gulf of Mexico. The whole area is subsiding at a few centimetres a year, so that older deltas and their varied deposits get covered by the sea and by the sediments of later deltas.

The pattern of terrestrial and marine sediments provides a good model for the repeating patterns of sediments in the Yoredales of northern England.

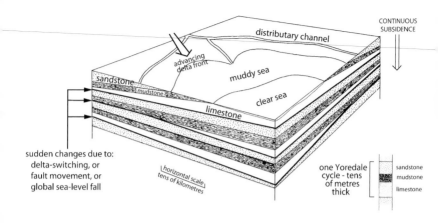

A simplified model of Yoredale cycles, based on the principle of a delta advancing into an area of clear sea. (The vertical scale is exaggerated.) Lower right – an idealised Yoredale cycle.

Each cycle starts with marine limestone, followed by mudstones as the delta approaches, and then coarser river sediments as the delta overwhelms the area. The whole system is slowly subsiding, preserving numerous repetitions of the cycles.

But there are (at least) two other influences to consider. The faults that define the blocks and troughs (Journal **6**) were active during the Carboniferous and had an effect on the subsidence and the kinds of sediment that were deposited. And though Britain during the Carboniferous was close to the equator, at the same time there were extensive and repeated glaciations in the southern hemisphere. Variations in the amount of ice on the polar continent created worldwide variations in sea level. (The same effect is a matter of concern at the present day, when global warming leads to melting of polar ice-caps and rapid rise in sea level.)

So the answer to the questions about how the rocks were formed is that there was an interaction of influences – local (the faulting), regional (the deltaic geography of northern England), and global (world-wide changes of sea level). And all in a context of prolonged subsidence to create a thick pile of sediments.

We shall see complete Yoredale cycles in Swinner Gill (2 km ahead on either of the routes through Swaledale).

THE RIVER SWALE BEFORE AND AFTER THE ICE AGE (Locs *D21-24*)

The first five Locations after leaving Keld are views of the River Swale and its tributaries. It's convenient to summarise now how they are related. Kisdon, the hill you can see southeast of Keld, is unusual among hills of the Dales in its square plan-view and in being detached from the main ridges. Its isolation developed from a change of course of the River Swale following the Ice Age.

Kisdon is surrounded on all four sides by valleys. The present course of the Swale is on the north and east sides. On the west side is a very small stream – the Skeb Skeugh – a misfit in the wide valley it occupies, and at its north end a completely dry valley. On the south side of Kisdon is Straw Beck – another small stream in a wide valley.

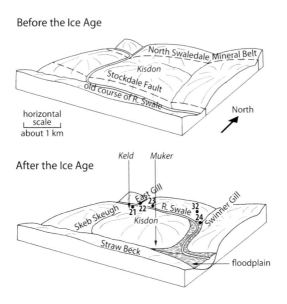

The course of the River Swale, before and after the Ice Age. Five Locations for seeing parts of the river system are numbered.

The likely history is that before the Ice Age the Swale was joined by East Gill at Keld and followed a course on the west and south sides of Kisdon. During the Ice Age a glacier widened the small valley on the north side of Kisdon. When the ice melted the Swale flowed straight on into this valley, and eroded it into a deep gorge. The west-to-east parts of both courses of the river were guided by more easily eroded rocks along the Stockdale Fault (Journal **6**) and the North Swaledale Mineral Belt.

THE WALK – KELD TO REETH

Leave Keld by the footpath along the right bank of the river.

THE COURSE OF THE RIVER SWALE

Loc. **D21**, NY 894 011. Stop briefly where there is a view to the southeast across fields towards Kisdon.

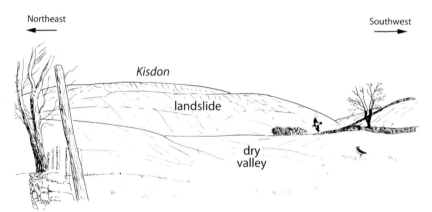

*Fig. **D21**. This very short dry valley, draining towards us, lies between the River Swale (in the deep valley behind you) and the valley of the Skeb Skeugh (behind the lapwings), draining southwards.*

The upper slopes of Kisdon are marked by a major landslide, which occurred after the end of the Ice Age.

Continue on the downhill path for 200 metres.

Loc. **D22**, NY 896 011, the footbridge over the River Swale. A limestone makes the bed of the Swale and the waterfall in East Gill. It can be examined here, but more conveniently in Locations 1½ km ahead.

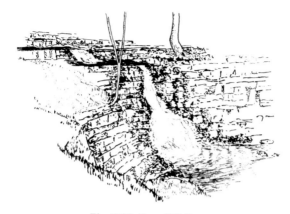

Fig. D22. East Gill Force.

The course of East Gill is from north to south. If it continued in that direction (as it probably did before erosion in the Ice Age changed the valley patterns) it would have flowed straight on into the dry valley of the last Location.

Walk on for another 300 metres, passing an exposure of 2 metres of black mudstone on the east side of the bridge over East Gill.

Loc. **D23**, NY 898 011, where the gorge of the River Swale comes into view.

Fig. D23/1. The whole volume of rock formerly in the gorge was eroded in the 10,000 years since the end of the Ice Age.

To the right of this view you can pick out the line of one of the faults of the North Swaledale Mineral Belt.

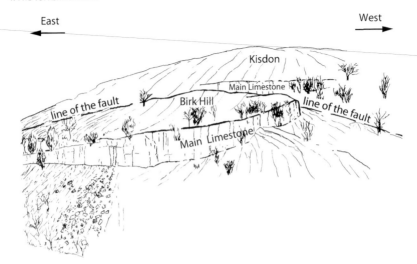

East ←

West →

Fig. D23/2. The fault is obscured by scree and vegetation, but runs through the gully between Birk Hill and the slopes of Kisdon. The block of Main Limestone that forms Birk Hill has probably slid downhill as a result of being detached from the main outcrop on Kisdon.

Continue along the track for ¾ km. Beldi Hill, to your left, in the North Swaledale Mineral Belt, was an important area for lead mining in the nineteenth century.

At the fork of the track at NY 905 009 you have a choice of two very different Routes to Reeth. The high-level Route (15 km), to the left, travels along the North Swaledale Mineral Belt, with plenty of evidence of the former mining industry. You might like to add an hour to the journey time, mainly in Swinner Gill, one km ahead. To the right is the valley Route (17 km) which follows the river. You could add half-an-hour to the journey time for river scenery and some deep geological structure.

CRACKPOT TO REETH – THE LOW-LEVEL ROUTE

Continue on the downward track for a total of ½ km from the junction of the paths.

The track crosses an active landslip. The rate of movement can be guessed from the curvature of the trunks of trees – clearly it is fast enough to match their rate of growth.

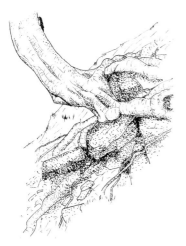

A struggle in progress – a tree tries both to stay upright and to keep its grip on the boulders of the slowly moving landslip.

MORE RIVER SCENERY

Loc. **D24**, NY 909 005, where the track crosses Swinner Gill at Fair Yew End. (The ruins of a smelt mill stand beside the stream.)

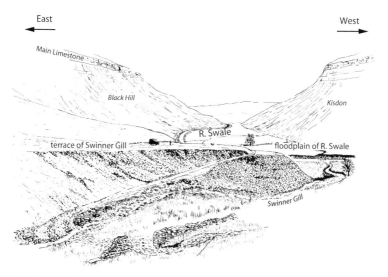

Fig. D24/1. View down the Swale valley on the east side of Kisdon. The shape of the valley sides was modified by the diversion of the river after the Ice Age (Journal 7). A terrace at the mouth of Swinner Gill is being eroded by the present-day stream.

CARBONIFEROUS SEDIMENTS

At the same Location a Yoredale sequence is exposed in and below the waterfall.

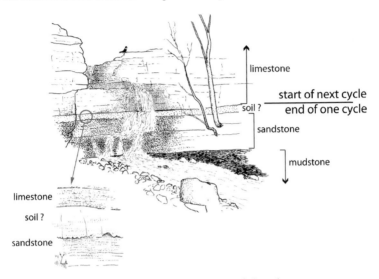

Fig. D24/2. Parts of two Yoredale cycles.

The curiously irregular boundary between the top two layers of the lower cycle suggests that the two rocks were closely related. The very tough rock overlying the sandstone was probably a soil. (At this time, 330 million years ago, Britain was near the equator. The soil would have been formed by strong leaching in the hot and wet climate – very different from our present-day conditions.)

An idealised Yoredale cycle, based on an advancing river delta, starts with a limestone and ends with a sandstone (Journal 7). It's worth looking closely at the sharply defined **bedding plane** between the possible soil (almost certainly formed on land) and the overlying limestone (made in clear sea water). A quick reminder of possible explanations for this change of environment – delta-switching, fault movement, global rise of sea level. This exposure alone can't tell us what was the cause, but the dramatic suddenness of the effect is clear.

One bed of the limestone contains solitary corals and brachiopod shells.

> *Continue along the track on the floodplain of the river. (After 3 km Ramps Holme Bridge gives an opportunity to cross the river to visit Muker.) The Route stays on the left bank. Another 2 km brings you to the elegant packhorse bridge at Ivelet.*

Ivelet Bridge.

THE STOCKDALE FAULT

Loc. **D25**, SD 933 978 to 937 980, from Ivelet Bridge to Shore Gill. This Location is spread over ½ km.

From Ivelet Bridge walk along the road on the left bank of the river for 300 metres, turn left uphill with the road, and in 50 metres turn right at the telephone box. A short road between houses leads to a footpath down into Shore Gill.

As you walk from Ivelet Bridge, notice the irregular dip directions of the Carboniferous rocks, first in a small fold on the south bank of the river downstream from Ivelet Bridge, then on the north side of the road, and finally in Shore Gill.

Though the folds are not much to look at, they are in sharp contrast to the extensive near-horizontal layers of the same rocks elsewhere (compare, for instance, Fig. **D23**) and so need some explanation. We are on the line of the Stockdale Fault, and the folds are the local expression of that large-scale structure. The Journal at Reeth gives more information.

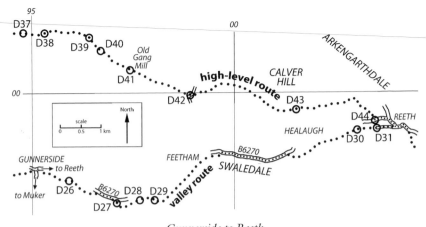

Gunnerside to Reeth.

FEATURES OF THE SWALE VALLEY, MAINLY TO DO WITH THE RIVER

The Main Limestone is still keeping us company, but now at the top of the valley sides, at 400-500 metres above sea level. In the valley we are walking at 250 metres, descending to 180 metres at Reeth. The Great Scar Limestone, our companion in Ravenstonedale, just fails to break surface at the bottom of the valley. Between the two limestones are rocks of the Yoredale cycles, with the harder layers making crag-and-ledge features on the valley sides.

From Shore Gill walk on into Gunnerside (1½ km). Part of the Route is at the top of a high bank eroded by the river.

Marble Scar. This is a local name – there is no marble rock here.

Gunnerside was a major mining centre up to the nineteenth century. Gunnerside Gill leads to the centre of the mining activity along the North Swaledale Mineral Belt.

*(If you want to change to the high-level Route for the rest of the Walk to Reeth, the nearest point is 3½ km up Gunnerside Gill at Loc. **D36**.)*

To continue on the low-level Route from the centre of Gunnerside, walk down the footpath in front of the King's Head and in 50 metres turn left on a footpath across fields on the floodplain of the River Swale. After 1 km, where the river cuts into its north bank, a track leads up to the road.

Loc. **D26**, SD 959 979, on the track from the meadows to the road.

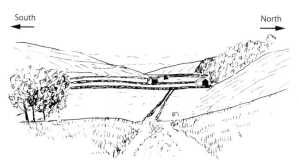

South ←   North →

*Fig. **D26**. The view back up the valley, showing the wide floodplain of the river (hidden by the trees on the left).*

Stay on the road for 1 km and then return to the left bank of the river. The next Location is 100 metres ahead.

Loc. **D27**, SD 970 973, the river-bank southwest of the house at Rowleth Wath.

*Fig. **D27/1**. A former course of the river is revealed as a channel-shape cut into older gravels. Later it was filled with dark peaty sand, most likely when it was in the floodplain of a new course of the river.*

Here, or at any place where you can see the boulders in the river-bed in a good light -

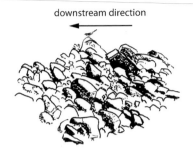

Fig. D27/2. Boulders inclined upstream.

Boulders in a fast-flowing stream are flipped over by the current, but with more difficulty if flat sides face upstream. This preferred orientation can be used in ancient sediments to determine the direction of flow of a stream.

Continue on the path beside the river. The next Location is in ¾ km.

Loc. **D28**, SD 977 975, on the upstream side of Isles Bridge.

Fig. D28. The bed of the river is wider here and there is the suggestion of an abandoned meander. Possibly the bridge made an obstruction that caused changes in the gradient and course of the river.

Walk on to cross the road at Isles Bridge and continue on the river-bank, which is here built up as a man-made levée (to protect the fields from floods).

Loc. **D29**, SD 980 975, ½ km below Isles Bridge, where the levée becomes a well-built stone wall capped with flagstones.

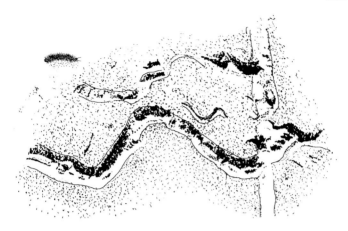

*Fig. **D29**. **Trace fossils** in a flagstone. (Trace fossils are the trails left by animals moving through unconsolidated sediment – the equivalent in Carboniferous time of scrawling one's name in the sand.)*

For the next 6 km the river flows in long straight reaches, alternately touching the south and the north banks. (See the Journal at Richmond.)

Stay on the river-bank for 1½ km, and then on the road for a straight stretch of 1½ km (parallel to one of the river reaches). At a wide parking area take the footpath to the right, back to the river-bank for a further 2 km. Where the river again approaches the north bank the path leads up to the next Location.

Loc. **D30**, SE 030 991, on the lower slopes of the valley near Reeth.

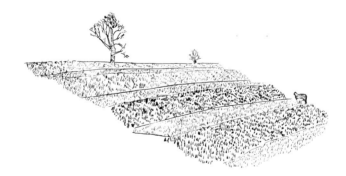

*Fig. **D30**. Lynchets, probably of mediaeval date. These are agricultural terraces, not to be confused with the crag-and-ledge features that result from alternating layers of hard and soft rock.*

Stay on the path for another ½ km.

Loc. **D31**, SE 035 991, with a good view of the River Swale. There is an intriguing combination of straight, meandering, and braided stretches of the river – see Fig. **D44**.

Walk on into Reeth (½ km).

CRACKPOT TO REETH – THE HIGH-LEVEL ROUTE

From the junction of the paths at NY 905 009 walk on for ½ km, passing the romantic ruins of Crackpot Hall (lived in till the middle of the twentieth century) and buildings associated with the Beldi Hill mines.

RIVER SCENERY

Loc. **D32**, NY 908 009, at Crackpot Hall.

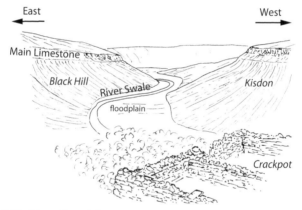

*Fig. **D32**. The valley of the River Swale, shaped by the diversion after the Ice Age (Journal 7). The wide floodplain is a more recent infill; much of it is rock eroded from Kisdon gorge, to the right of this scene.*

Continue on the track for ½ km. A small exposure 100 metres east of Crackpot Hall is muddy limestone with a few shell fragments.

SWINNER GILL – SEDIMENTS, FAULTS, AND MINERAL VEINS

Loc. **D33**, NY 910 009, by the gate at the top of the path.

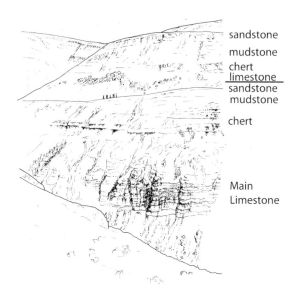

*Fig. **D33**. View into Swinner Gill from the west side, showing two complete Yoredale cycles (Journal 7). The lower one, from the Main Limestone to the next sandstone above, is about 50 metres thick.*

Walk on for a further ½ km down the indistinct path into Swinner Gill.

Loc. **D34**, NY 911 012, near the bridge across Swinner Gill. Here you are in the centre of the North Swaledale Mineral Belt. It's worth spending a little time here to see the Carboniferous rocks and what's left of the mineral **veins** which cut them.

If you are short of time you could look at some of the Locations described here. To spend more time (for instance when the valley is a very pleasant sun-trap), you could look in more detail at the rocks in the stream-bed between the bridge and the big limestone cliff 100 metres upstream.

The rocks are cut by a number of faults. Their effects can be easily seen, as the Main Limestone is repeated three times, each time making a distinct gorge. From south to north, the limestone makes the gorge below the point where East Grain joins the main gill, then the shallow gorge above the bridge, and at the top the big cliff which starts the upper gorge.

The mineral veins followed the faults because the broken rocks in or near the faults provided easy access for the hot fluids that deposited the **ores**.

Loc. **D34/1**. The view up East Grain. The valley is eroded along the line of the mineral veins.

*Fig. **D34/1**. The view shows a mine entrance and some former mine buildings.*

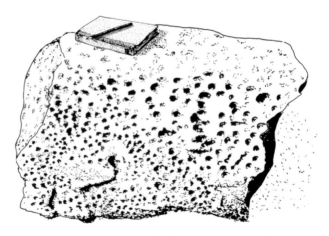

The dimpled surface of this limestone was made by acid rain-water running over its surface.

Loc. **D34/2**, 5 metres below the bridge, where a metre-wide trench cuts across the stream-bed. (This is best seen from the east side of the stream.) The trench marks the course of a mineral vein, which was emplaced along the line of a fault.

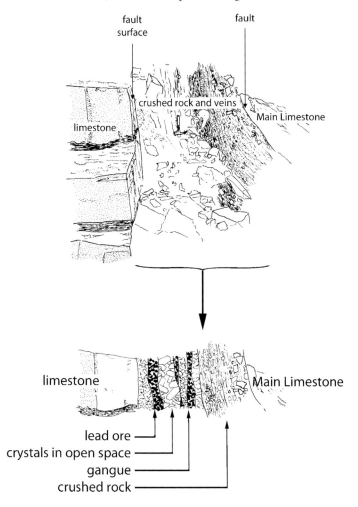

*Fig. **D34/2**. Mineral vein in Swinner Gill. All the valuable ore has been removed by mining, leaving the very smooth fault surface on the left and crushed limestone on the right. Inset – an impression of what the vein might have looked like. **Gangue** is the term for the minerals of no economic value compared with the ore.*

The Main Limestone on the right of the drawing continues in the gorge upstream from this Location.

Walk 100 metres upstream to the prominent limestone cliff.

On the way you cross varied rock-types of the Carboniferous – chert (a very hard black rock made of fine-grained silica), sandstone, and black mudstone – and some of the small folds and faults which cut them. You will get a clear impression of the complicated structure of the North Swaledale Mineral Belt.

Loc. **D34/3**. The limestone cliff and gorge 100 metres above the bridge in Swinner Gill.

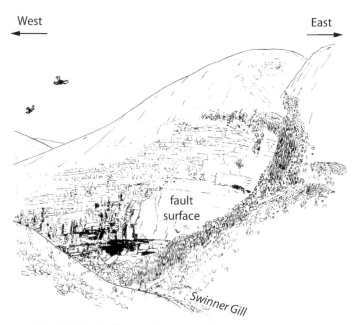

West East

*Fig. **D34/3**. Looking up Swinner Gill from near the bridge.*

At the bridge you were standing near the top of the Main Limestone. The base of the same limestone makes the dark shadow at the bottom of the cliff. The displacement of the fault is more than the thickness of the Main Limestone, or about half the height of the hillside.

The faults at Locs **D34/2** and **D34/3** are the easiest to see in the whole length of the Walk. You can even put the flat of your hand on the surface where the rocks slid past each other. There is more about the faults and mineral veins in the Journal at Reeth.

Loc. **D34/4**. The base of the cliff shows the base of the Main Limestone, which is also the base of a Yoredale cycle.

Main Limestone

silty sandstone

black mudstone

sandstone

*Fig. **D34/4**. The sharply defined junction of the silty sandstone with the overlying limestone marks the sudden switch of conditions from sandy river to clear sea.*

Think about what happened here – change of direction of a deltaic river, fault movement, or global rise of sea level? Or some combination of factors? We don't think it's possible to tell from this exposure alone. But it shows how dramatically a change of sea level and the position of a coastline can alter an environment – an object lesson for the current debate about global warming!

SWINNER GILL KIRK

If the stream is low, a careful scramble for 100 metres up the limestone gorge brings you to Swinner Gill Kirk – a cave which was used for religious services by Dissenters in the late seventeenth century.

Swinner Gill Kirk is the cave at the bottom left of the waterfall. The cave slopes down into the hillside, following the bedding planes of the Main Limestone.

The next Location is 2 km ahead. Return to the bridge and follow the path up East Grain.

Beside the path are areas of tufa – calcium carbonate deposited where springs of limestone-saturated water have evaporated. (This is in effect the low-temperature natural equivalent of the scale that forms in your kettle in a hard-water area.)

At the top of East Grain the path joins a good track. At two small cairns, where the track veers to the right, take the path down to the left.

MINERAL VEINS

Loc. **D35**, NY 933 014, where an impressive chasm comes into view on the east side of the path.

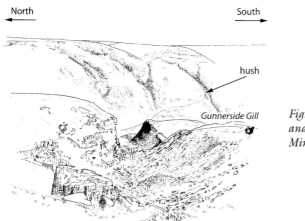

*Fig. **D35**. North Hush and Lownathwaite Mines.*

The irregular gully is the course of a mineral vein, extracted in part by "hushing" – that is, damming water at the top of the hill, then breaking the dam to release a flood of water to expose and erode the ore and carry it downhill. (Sand-and-water play on a grand scale, but with a serious – and probably underpaid – purpose!) The quantity of detritus must have added enormously to the load of sediment carried by the stream in the valley below. Three more hushes can be seen on the opposite side of Gunnerside Gill.

The next Location is ¾ km ahead. Continue on the path to the bottom of the valley.

Loc. **D36**, NY 937 017, Gunnerside Beck and Blakethwaite Smelt mill.

West   East

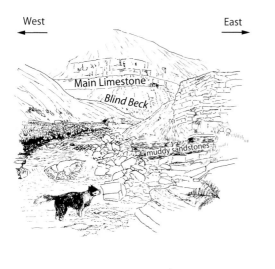

*Fig. **D36**. Gunnerside Beck, looking upstream to Blind Beck. Muddy sandstones are exposed on the right of the stream.*

Part of the ruins of Blakethwaite Smelt mill (looking more suited to use as a church than Swinner Gill Kirk did). The path to the top of the valley rises behind the mill.

There are several paths and miners' tracks to the next Location, 1½ km ahead. You need to get to the top of the valley side above Blakethwaite. Climb steeply out of the Gill by short zig-zags to a good path rising gently to the right. After ½ km turn left on a path up a steep gully (Bunton Hush). At the top of the hill turn right on a good track.

Loc. **D37**, NY 948 014, at the highest point on the track.

Gunnerside Gill and the areas around show intensive effects of the lead-mining. All that remains now is the ruins of buildings, mine entrances and pits, and wide areas of waste rock, such as here on Melbecks Moor. According to your point of view this is industrial desolation, fascinating archaeology, or fine open country.

On a clear day you can see 20-30 km away to the south: (from right to left) Yockenthwaite Moor, Buckden Pike, and the top of the ridge of Great Whernside. All are formed of Carboniferous rocks in the Askrigg Block.

Fig. D37/1. A relic of the lead-mining industry – a portable crushing machine stands like a beached whale on a barren landscape of mine waste.

The absence of plants, more than a hundred years after mining ended, shows that the ground is still toxic. The crushed rock is a useful source of gravel; in resurfaced tracks you can sometimes see tiny grey crystals of lead ore (galena, lead sulphide) brightly reflecting the sunlight.

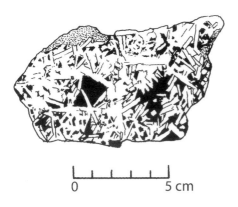

Fig. D37/2. At the same Location, many of the boulders contain white platy crystals of barite (barium sulphate). It is distinctly heavier than ordinary rocks such as limestone – try hefting a lump of it.

Here the barite is a **gangue** mineral in the veins that were mined for the lead ore; in some other places it is worked as an industrial mineral for its own value. (You may be looking at some barite as you read this – one of its uses is for making paper whiter and heavier.)

Walk on along the track for ½ km to the extensive waste heaps of Old Gang Mines.

CARBONIFEROUS SEDIMENTS

Loc. **D38**, NY 953 014, an exposure of limestone beside the track at the waste tips for Old Gang Mine.

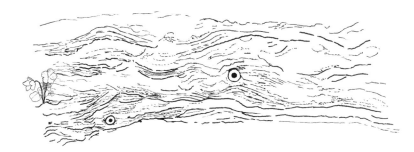

*Fig. **D38**. Limestone with ripples (and rare "polo mints" of sea lily stems).*

This was the deposit of a clear sea with enough wave or current energy to make the ripples, but too much energy for most animals to live in. The few broken shells came from a calmer part of this marine environment.

As you walk on to the next Location, 1¼ km ahead, you can see extensive workings on the line of another mineral vein ½ km to the north.

Loc. **D39**, NY 964 013, Level House Bridge.

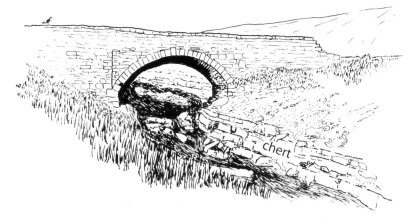

*Fig. **D39**. The foundations of the bridge are on a thick layer of bedded **chert**.*

This very hard rock is made of fine-grained silica (chemically the same as a sandstone, but its origin is marine and probably organic). It is part of the Yoredale sequence, the equivalent of a limestone in the cycle of rock-types.

Continue downhill for ½ km.

Loc. **D40**, NY 967 010, at the point where the path divides.

*Fig. **D40**. An easily accessible exposure of the Main Limestone.*

The well-developed columnar jointing makes the rock easy to distinguish from a distance. The rock is made entirely of shell fragments, with a few pieces of sea lily. The inset shows a detail of the rasp-like surface.

Continue along the track for 1 km.

OLD GANG SMELT MILL

Loc. **D41**, NY 974 005, Old Gang Smelt mill is a Scheduled Ancient Monument. Production of lead ended in 1898 when competition from foreign sources made it no longer economic.

*Fig. **D41/1**. A mine entrance beside the track 200 metres west of the smelt mill. Extracting the mineral vein from the surface produced the gully above the entrance. There are many tens of kilometres of mine workings in Swaledale and the surrounding areas.*

*Fig. **D41/2**. The lower end of a chimney at Old Gang Smelt mill. The chimney is 750 metres long, and rises 150 metres to the top of Healaugh Crag, to the north.*

*Fig. **D41/3**. Old Gang smelt mill.*

Huge chimneys like the one shown in Fig. **D41/2** increased the efficiency of smelting. They also carried some of the noxious fumes away from the work place.

The pillars of the peat store on the hillside above Old Gang Smelt mill.

Stay on the track for another 1½ km, to where it joins a tarmac road.

Loc. **D42**, SD 989 999, Surrender Bridge.

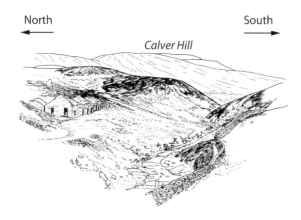

North ←   South →

Calver Hill

*Fig. **D42**. The ruins of Surrender smelt mill beside Barney Beck.*

Take the footpath across the moor on the north side of the smelt mill. After crossing Cringley Bottom follow the footpath above the fields. This leads to a track to Thirns. From there bear left and uphill to Moorcock Cottage. The next Location (2½ km from Surrender Bridge) is ¼ km beyond the cottage.

184

Loc. **D43**, SE 015 996, piles of stones beside the track.

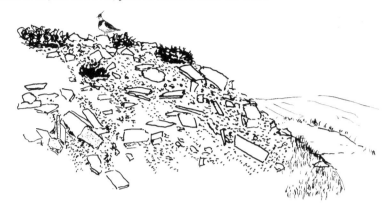

*Fig. **D43**. Waste rock from workings for stone slate. The usable rock was part of a thick sandstone which makes up most of the waste.*

This is the first exposure of sandstone we have seen since we were in Swinner Gill. The Yoredale sequences of limestone, mudstone, and sandstone are still here, but the limestones are more resistant to erosion and make the more prominent crags.

The next Location is 2½ km further. Stay on the track, keeping the fields to your right. After 1¼ km the track bends left; at this point walk half-left towards the corner of a field-wall. Follow the wall to a gate into a green (but stony) lane. Where the lane bends left go straight ahead through a gate onto a footpath to Reeth School.

Loc. **D44**, SE 034 993, on the roadside at the school.

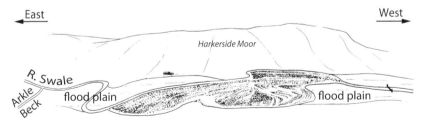

*Fig. **D44**. The River Swale flows into view from a long straight reach to the right, breaks into a combination of meandering, braided, and straight stretches in the centre, and continues downstream in a wide meander. (The width of the floodplain is exaggerated in the drawing.)*

A major tributary – Arkle Beck – joins the Swale to the left of the drawing, adding to the spread of sediment in the main valley. This decreases the gradient of the Swale on the upstream side. The varying shapes of the river are adaptations to its own widely varying rates of flow.

Walk down the road into Reeth, where the two Routes through Swaledale reunite.

185

JOURNAL 8 – REETH

Reeth Green.

THE STOCKDALE FAULT (Loc. *D25*).

The Stockdale Fault is a feature of the Carboniferous rocks from its western end, where it butts up against the Dent Fault (Journal **6**), to Reeth. The nearest we came to seeing the Fault was at Loc. **D25** on the low-level Route, where the Carboniferous rocks are folded – an anomaly from the usual nearly horizontal layers. The folds are the result of movement in the Lower Palaeozoic Basement.

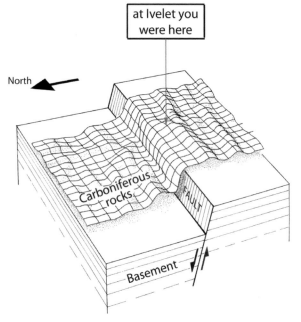

A simplified model (based on two piles of books and a checkered cloth) of the situation at Ivelet, showing how a fault in basement rocks can produce folds in rocks at a higher level.

The River Swale from Muker to Reeth runs parallel to the Stockdale Fault, and its course was probably determined by the easier erosion of the deformed rocks along the line of the fault.

MINES AND MINING

On the high-level Route through Swaledale we walked along 15 km of one of the most intensely mineralised parts of the North Swaledale Mineral Belt. Names like Swinner Gill, Lownathwaite, Gunnerside, Old Gang, and Surrender had even greater significance to the miners and mine-owners than they do to us today.

Finding, extracting, and processing lead ore started in Roman times, reached a peak in the nineteenth century, and was followed by a rapid decline as foreign ores became available. The history of the industry is one of hard social and economic conditions, physical toil and short life expectancy, heroism and tragedy. It has led to intense pride and love for the dale and all it gives to those who live here.

HOW THE MINERAL VEINS WERE FORMED (Loc. D34).

Suppose you had collected a sample of every rock you have seen on the Walk, mixed them all together, and made a chemical analysis of the mixture – the result would be very similar to the average chemical composition of the Earth's continents. Oxygen and silicon would predominate (most rocks are made of silicates), followed by aluminium, iron, and calcium. Many of the chemical elements in everyday use would be present in tiny amounts, measured in parts per million (ppm). (One ppm is the same as one gram in a tonne, or 0.0001 of a per cent. You could picture it as like searching for one particular grain of sand in a bucketful.) As examples: zinc forms 70 ppm of average continental crust, copper 55 ppm, lead 13 ppm, tin 2 ppm, while silver and gold form only 0.07 and 0.004 ppm.

Trace elements become useful ores by a great variety of methods, some of them very different in character from anything that can be seen in everyday Earth processes. We will describe just one – the formation of the ores of the North Swaledale Mineral Belt. Although lead has been mined here for 2000 years, we have only recently begun to understand how the ores were made.

The lead ores occur in steep or vertical sheets (**veins**), following joints or faults in the layered rocks of the Carboniferous. These rocks rest unconformably on the Lower Palaeozoic basement, which significantly includes large bodies of 400-million-year-old granite. The date of the mineralisation was probably Permian – about 300 million years ago. Although the granites had been exposed at the Earth's surface during the erosion that followed the Caledonian mountain-building, 100 million years later they were still hot enough to drive large-scale convection of fluids in the Earth's crust. (And at the present day, buried granites still contain enough heat to be sources of geothermal energy.)

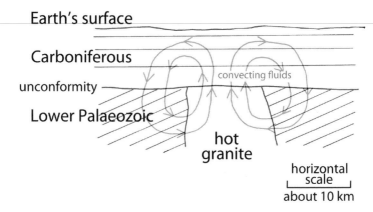

The convecting fluids passed through many different rocks, even involving groundwater from near the Earth's surface.

The heated fluids dissolved some of the tiny amounts of trace elements from huge volumes of rock, and deposited them as minerals in cooler areas. Because of the involvement of hot water (up to 200°C) such mineral deposits are called "hydrothermal".

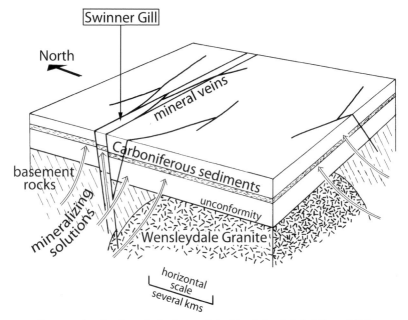

Cartoon showing how the lead ores of the North Swaledale Mineral Belt may be related to convecting fluids near the buried Wensleydale Granite.

This is a simplified explanation. To hint at deeper levels of complexity:

- Many of the ore and gangue minerals are very insoluble. The interaction of more than one kind of fluid, with different sources, at the site of deposition is likely.

- The circulating fluids were selective in their power of dissolving and carrying particular chemical elements.

- The banded structure of many of the ores (Fig. **34/2**) shows that their formation was episodic, with different minerals deposited at different times.

THE WALK – REETH TO RICHMOND

The next Location is 2 km ahead. Leave Reeth by the road to Richmond, and 200 metres after the bridge across Arkle Beck go right onto a footpath through fields to Grinton Bridge.

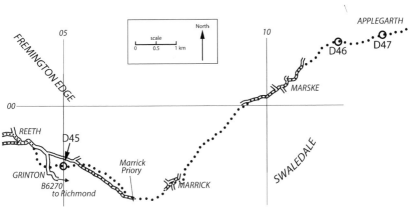

Reeth to Applegarth.

A stone wall flattened by a flood of the Swale – a reminder that the floodplain is as much part of the river system as is the more restricted channel. Grinton Bridge is in the background.

Continue on the left bank of the river for ½ km from Grinton Bridge.

Loc. **D45**, SE 050 986, or anywhere with a view to Ewelop Hill – the low ridge projecting from the north side of the valley.

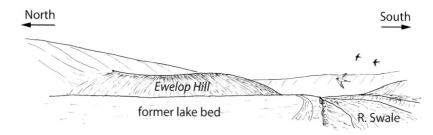

*Fig. **D45**. Ewelop Hill (without the trees) from the west.*

This ridge of boulder clay is part of a **terminal moraine** marking a temporary halt in the retreat of the glacier which formerly occupied Swaledale. It would have extended all across the valley. The flat ground you are standing on looks like a river terrace, but in this context is more likely to have been the bed of a lake temporarily dammed by the moraine.

Beyond Ewelop Hill a short climb leads to a minor road to Marrick Priory (1½ km). Just beyond the Priory turn left onto a path which leads up the Nuns' Steps to Marrick (1 km from the Priory). The next Location is 6 km further on.

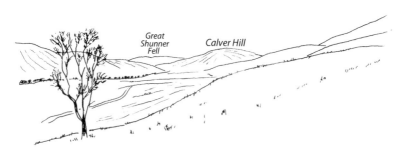

The view back up Swaledale from Marrick Priory.

The Nuns' Causey.

From the top of the Steps keep straight on into Marrick village. Turn right at the road junction at the east end of the village. After 150 metres turn left onto a green lane, leading to a footpath through fields.

From Marrick, after 1 km a steep descent to the track from the farm at Nun Cote Nook marks the outcrop of the Main Limestone.

Continue across fields to reach the road at Hardstiles top. From here walk down the road into Marske. Take the road across the bridge. After ½ km, at a left bend of the road, turn right on a footpath across fields towards the crags of Applegarth Scar.

Loc. **D46**, NZ 118 015, where the footpath joins the track to Applegarth at a small cairn.

*Fig. **D46/1**. The Main Limestone at the west end of Applegarth Scar. It has the same kind of columnar jointing we have seen before.*

191

From here there is a fine view back up Swaledale.

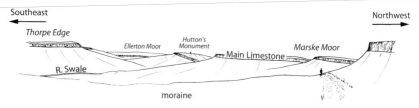

*Fig. **D46/2**. The Main Limestone shapes the landscape.*

Continue along the track and footpaths for 1 km.

Loc. **D47**, NZ 129 016, Deep Dale, near Low and High Applegarth.

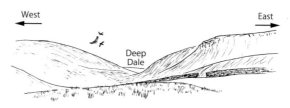

*Fig. **D47**. This dry valley was eroded at the end of the Ice Age, when an ice-dammed lake to the north drained suddenly across Applegarth Scar. There must have been an impressive waterfall for a few weeks or months.*

About 200 metres east of Deep Dale mine waste-heaps high above the path mark the position of a small lead vein. This is the last we shall see of the mining industry which was so important in the industrial history of Swaledale.

Continue along the footpath for ½ km, keeping at about the same level below the Scar.

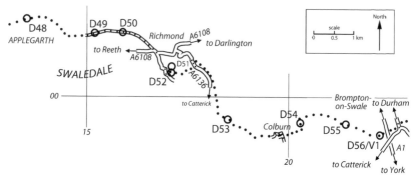

Applegarth to Brompton-on-Swale.

Loc. **D48**, NZ 135 018, near East Applegarth.

*Fig. **D48**. Looking east down Swaledale. The irregular ground along the line of the path is either moraine or landslips from the Main Limestone in the cliffs to the left.*

Stay on the footpath through Whitecliffe Wood, leading into a road. The next Location, 2 km ahead, is any point at which you get a clear view to the south and east.

Loc. **D49**, near NZ 152 015, on the road at Whitcliffe Farm. From here we get a first sight of the Vale of Mowbray and in the far distance the North York Moors.

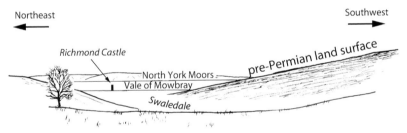

*Fig. **D49**. The view (exaggerated vertically) to the southeast from near Whitcliffe Farm.*

We are here standing on rocks of the Carboniferous. The bedrock of the Vale is Permo-Triassic, and that of the Moors is Jurassic. The sediments of the Permo-Triassic and Jurassic originally covered the Pennines to a thickness of a few thousand metres. All that thickness of rock has been eroded away, long before the Ice Age.

The slope of the long straight skyline to the southeast is near-enough parallel with the dip of the base of the Permian where it outcrops to the east of Richmond. That slope is almost a resurrection of the 300-million-year-old land surface – the Variscan unconformity – on which the Permian rocks were deposited. (It is of course not the exact surface because it has been lowered by later erosion.) Journal **10** gives more detail.

Continue along the road for 1 km. At the bottom of the first hill, another post-glacial valley, like the one that made the break in Applegarth Scar, comes in from the left.

Loc. **D50**, NZ 159 015, near Belleisle Farm on the left of the road. About here you get the clearest view of Round Howe among the trees on the opposite side of the Swale valley.

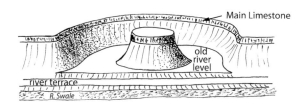

*Fig. **D50**. Simplified drawing (without the trees) of the deeply incised dry meander of the River Swale at Round Howe. (The meander core stands proudly in its bowl like a plum pudding in a dish of custard!)*

The cap of Round Howe and the cliffs on the outside of the meander are the Main Limestone. As we have often seen, the Main Limestone is resistant to erosion. The unusual shape of its outcrops here suggests that the meander was first formed when the river was at the level of the top of the cliffs. The present straight course of the river probably developed when the meander had eroded down to the level of the nearly flat platform that extends round the back of the Howe.

Continue along the road into Richmond (1½ km).

JOURNAL 9 – RICHMOND

The town is often called "The Gateway to Swaledale" (or even "to the Dales", though there are other contenders). We shall pass eastwards through the gateway – those who love the Dales would say "in the wrong direction" – to move on to the Vale of Mowbray and the distant North York Moors.

Richmond Market Place.

The Carboniferous rocks we have been walking over all the way from Shap continue for another 5 km, but as we walk eastwards from Richmond the rocks and scenery of the Dales gradually sink below a cover of boulder clay. We shall move from hilly pastoral country, with open moorland and small fields marked out by stone walls, to large flat or gently rolling arable fields bounded by hedges.

THE CARBONIFEROUS ROCKS OF SWALEDALE

The Main Limestone has been with us most of the way from Kirkby Stephen. Let's briefly consider what it tells us about the Carboniferous environment. It is one of the most extensive units of the Yoredale cycles – from Weardale in the north to Ribblesdale in the south (65 km) and from Nine Standards Rigg in the west to Richmond in the east (35 km). Any animal fortunate enough to have lived in the shallow warm clear tropical sea that deposited the limestone would have had a variety of resource-rich niches to choose from. These ranged from coral reefs and banks of sea lilies to shell sand (Loc. **D40**) and soft calcite mud on the sea floor.

If the animal could have put its head above the waves it might have seen the Scottish mountains far to the north, and the slowly advancing deltas which would eventually overwhelm the area. As the land approached, the sea became muddier, challenging the survival of marine animal and plant species. After thousands of years the delta front arrived and rivers spread sand, silt, and mud across the whole area. On the low-lying land there were tropical forests and a fauna of air-breathing animals. That completes one Yoredale cycle. The possible causes of the repetition of cycles were discussed in Journal 7.

The pattern of cycles lasted for much of the 60 million years of the Carboniferous. Over time there was a slow change to a dominance of the land environments, so that marine limestones became less common and coal more common, leading to the Coal Measures which give the Carboniferous its name.

THE RIVER SWALE

The west-to-east course of the river, from Kisdon to Reeth, was carved into the bedrock along the line of the Stockdale Fault (Journals **6** and **7**). The valley was widened and deepened by a glacier during the Ice Age. Melting of the glacier produced boulder clay and some terminal moraines (Loc. **D45**). The present river, well known for its occasional and dangerous spates (many lives have been lost in the past), spends its time either in its usual course or spread across the floodplain.

A feature of the river is its long straight reaches, crossing diagonally from one side of the floodplain to the other. (We are now referring to straight lengths up to 2 km, not the 15 km length of the Dale as a whole.) For comparison, Whitsundale Beck (the tributary of the upper Swale, seen by travellers on the Blue Route across Nine Standards Rigg) makes a typical meandering pattern:

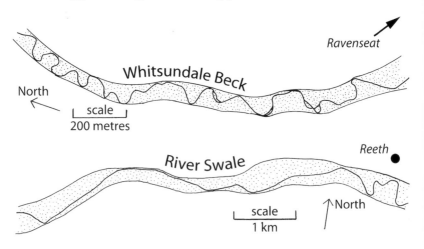

Parts of Whitsundale Beck and the River Swale, with their floodplains. (The two maps are drawn at different scales.)

The course of a river is controlled by factors such as its energy (the volume of water and how fast it flows) and the resistance to its flow (the sediment load and the ease of eroding the river banks). The vigorous floods of the upper Swale force the river into the most direct course.

THE WALK – RICHMOND
TO CATTERICK BRIDGE

From the centre of Richmond, head for the bridge on the south side of the town (NZ 170 006). There are many attractive routes – we have used the broad walk on the south side of the castle.

Loc. **D51**, NZ 171 007, below the castle perimeter wall.

*Fig. **D51**. Stonework so skilfully built into the Carboniferous bedrock that it's hard to distinguish one from the other.*

On the south side of Richmond Bridge turn left to the football ground.

Loc. **D52**, NZ 171 005.

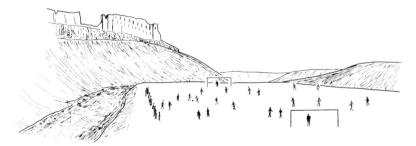

*Fig. **D52**. The floodplain of the River Swale at Richmond (without the trees). The castle walls provide the grandstand.*

197

The next Location is 2½ km ahead. Continue on the path until it joins the A6136 road. Turn left, and in 100 metres turn right past the former railway station and walk along the old line beside the river. After ½ km cross the cattle grid and bear right onto the path past the sewage works. The path then climbs through woodland high above the river.

Easby Abbey.

Loc. **D53**, SE 185 995, anywhere giving a view through the trees.

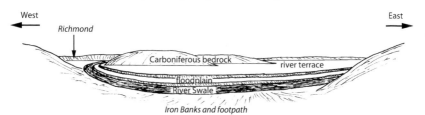

*Fig. **D53**. A panoramic view (nearly 180°) from the path above the River Swale, looking across it to the north.*

Downstream from Richmond the valley of the River Swale becomes wider and less gorge-like. A large part of the floor of the valley is a terrace, about 5 metres above the narrow floodplain. This simple scene shows a four-stage history: erosion into the bedrock (during Ice Age time, making the wide valley), then deposition (the terrace), followed by erosion (cutting into the terrace), and deposition (the river and its floodplain).

This Location provides our final (and distant) view of the Carboniferous rocks we have been walking over for the last 90 km. The Carboniferous bedrock of the hill in the middle distance dips gently to the east (right). The ridge 3 km away on the right is made by the Main Limestone. It comes to within 1 km of the base of the Permian, just beyond the right side of the drawing (see Journal **10**).

Stay on the path to the remains of Hagg Farm, then briefly on a track down to the left, and up obliquely across the next field. The path stays within fields to the road through Colburn village. Towards the end of the village follow the road to the right and take the first turn to the left. At the end of the second field turn left along the field edge and then right along the top of the river bank.

Loc. **D54**, SE 203 994, anywhere beside the path. It's worth taking a quick look at some of the cobbles in the fields here. They are smoothed and rounded, with scratches indicating their origin from boulder clay – a clue to the scenery around you.

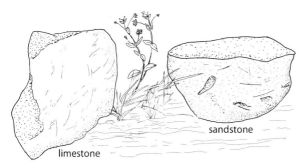

*Fig. **D54**. Two **erratics** from the boulder clay. The limestone has taken a better polish than the sandstone. Both cobbles are broken pieces of larger boulders.*

The relatively flat scenery is our first close-up view of the great expanse of boulder clay that covers much of the Vale of Mowbray.

Walk on along the path at the top of the river-bank, joining a tarmac road at St Giles Farm for a few metres, and then again beside fields.

Loc. **D55**, SE 214 994, near St Giles Farm, or anywhere along the high river-bank where you get a view across the river. You can see the three kinds of land surface that make the Vale of Mowbray.

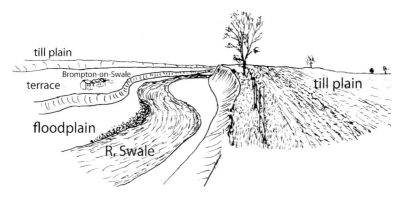

*Fig. D55. The river near Brompton-on-Swale. The floodplain is next to the river. The village is built on the terrace. The higher not-quite-level surface is a **till plain** (explained in Journal 10).*

Continue on the path until it leads down to the river at the A1 road, then under the bridge, across the next field, up the steps to the old railway bridge across the Swale, and down to the footpath on the north bank of the river.

Loc. **D56/V1**, SE 222 991, Catterick Bridge over the River Swale. It is about here that we cross the unconformable boundary between the Carboniferous and the Permian. There is nothing to see on the ground, even though the bedrock is covered by only a few metres of boulder clay and river deposits. At this point, with no pictorial memorial and just the cluster of roads and a dismantled railway to act as a marker, we close the chapter on the Yorkshire Dales. But hopefully with many pleasant memories.

JOURNAL 10 – CATTERICK BRIDGE

NO COAL AT CATTERICK – THE VARISCAN UNCONFORMITY (AGAIN)

We have just crossed, for the fourth time on the Walk, the boundary between the Carboniferous and the Permian – and we still haven't seen the real thing! On this side of the Pennines the unconformity is again covered by superficial deposits, so it can't be examined directly. However, the indirect evidence for its existence is compelling, though it needs a little explanation:

You may remember from Journal **6** that the boundary is an **unconformity**. It was the land surface made by erosion following the Variscan mountain-building – the result of collision of the Laurasia and Gondwana continents 300 million years ago. Several-thousand-metres thickness of Carboniferous rocks younger than the Main Limestone (including Coal Measures) originally covered northern England and southern Scotland. One effect of the Variscan deformation was to fold the Carboniferous rocks in the Richmond area. The subsequent erosion removed the Coal Measures. We can show this on a map, most easily understood with North to the left.

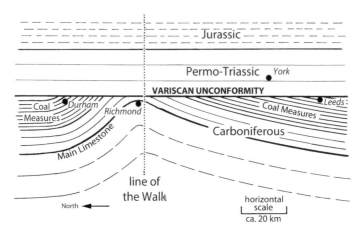

A very simplified map of a wide area of northern England. This is the view you would get (but vertically exaggerated in the drawing) if you were looking east along the line of the Walk from a balloon high above the west end of Swaledale.

You can work out the history of the area by reading the drawing from the bottom upwards along the line of the walk:

1. Carboniferous rocks were deposited as continuous horizontal layers, covering the whole area.

2. The Carboniferous rocks were folded by the Variscan mountain-building.

3. The layers were eroded to make a new land surface (the Variscan unconformity), cutting down almost to the Main Limestone. This is the 300-million-year-old land surface that we saw from Loc. **D49**.

4. Permo-Triassic and Jurassic rocks were deposited.

5. All the rocks were tilted down to the east (away from us in the drawing) and then eroded, so as to reveal them as they are now.

So, if it had not been for the Variscan mountain-building and unconformity the scenery east of Catterick Bridge would be very different. We would be walking through the towns and villages of a coal-mining area like those of County Durham and south Yorkshire. The Walk might not have been so scenically attractive and agricultural, but it would have been more varied, including important economic resources.

INTRODUCTION TO THE VALE OF MOWBRAY

The history we have just worked out created a landscape very similar to what we see today. The Permo-Triassic rocks were much more easily eroded than either the Carboniferous or the Jurassic, making a broad valley between the Dales and the Moors:

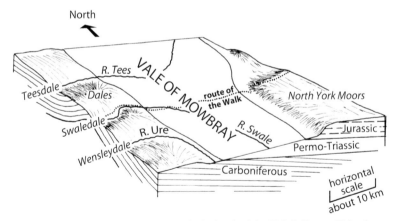

Cartoon of the Vale of Mowbray. The bedrock of the Vale is Permo-Triassic.

During the Ice Age, glaciers from the Pennines and Scotland spread southwards down the Vale of Mowbray. When the ice sheet melted, the rock material contained in it was deposited as boulder clay. (Much of the rock eroded from the Dales is now in the Vale.) At the present day the Dales and Moors are still largely areas of erosion. In effect, the scenery of the Vale of Mowbray, protected from erosion by a thin blanket of boulder clay, is an older part of the landscape than either the Dales or the Moors.

Alfred Wainwright remarks that some walkers may find the Vale of Mowbray enjoyable for the placid rural landscape, while those who prefer the rough hills may think it tedious. One of the pleasures of geology is the interest provided by almost any kind of scenery. What you look for, and how to understand it, changes according to the way the rocks and scenery present themselves.

The surface of the Vale of Mowbray is gently undulating, at a small range of heights – 40 to 80 metres above sea level. It is a **till plain** (till is the term for deposits like boulder clay formed directly from ice without being carried by meltwater). The boulder clay is up to 40 metres thick, hiding the desert sandstones of the underlying Permo-Triassic bedrock. Rivers and their floodplains have locally eroded into the boulder clay, but not down to the bedrock.

To simplify your understanding of the rocks and scenery of the Vale, there are just three kinds of situation. If you are walking on a flat area close to a stream or river, you are walking on a floodplain. If the ground is flat and you are 5-10 metres above the river, you are on a river terrace. If the terrain is nearly (but not quite) flat, you are walking on the till plain. Any areas that project above the general level of the Vale (like the heights of the North York Moors, which get more impressive as you get nearer) are bedrock.

We illustrate the journey with some typical views – you will be able to match the drawings to the passing scenery several times as you walk on. There are just two formal Locations, marking significant events in the passing of geological time as we walk over the unseen bedrock.

THE VALE OF MOWBRAY – A PICTURE GALLERY

The River Swale and its terraces

Fig. V2. A lake in a former gravel pit near Catterick Bridge (SE 232 995), now used for fishing. Over the years land use changed from farming to gravel extraction and then to the leisure industry.

Fig. V3. The path (SE 246 996, near Bolton-on-Swale) climbs 6 metres from the floor of the old gravel pit to the level of the original terrace. All that gravel is now in roads and buildings in northern England.

The boundary between a river terrace and the till plain

Fig. V4. Bolton Beck (SE 257 992, near Bolton-on-Swale). The beck flows along the boundary between the gently hilly till plain and the flat terrace of the River Swale. The river is 1¼ km to the right of this scene.

The till plain

The gently undulating scenery gives (on a clear day) some surprisingly long views, even from small rises. As you travel, you can measure your progress by the distance to the receding Dales and the advancing Moors.

Fig. V5. A general view (SE 296 977, near Stanhowe Cottages) of the Vale of Mowbray – broad low hills, wide fields, hedges, woods.

Fig. V6. A green lane (SE 329 978, near Danby Wiske).

Fig. V7. Ploughed field (SE 334 979, near Danby Wiske). The deep rich soil is derived from the underlying boulder clay.

*Fig. V8. **Drumlins** near Oaktree Farm, SE 357 987. The drawing is slightly exaggerated vertically and most of the trees have been left out, so the drumlins look a little more impressive in the drawing than they really are. This is "basket-of-eggs" topography (compare with Fig. R12).*

It isn't possible to say why the ice sheet just here (and not at other places in the Vale) was able to mould the boulder clay into drumlin shapes, but perhaps the ice was flowing, rather than melting in place.

Fig. V9. A drainage ditch near Moor House (SE 377 994), with boulder clay showing in the recently cleaned sides.

Fig. V10. A low-lying part of a field in the till plain near Sydal Lodge (NZ 422 013). Lake sediments were deposited here when the ice melted, and it is still a pond today.

5. THE VALE OF MOWBRAY

The Walk continues with the low-lying scenery of the Vale, formed by glacial and river deposits covering rocks of Permian and Triassic age.

THE WALK – CATTERICK BRIDGE TO INGLEBY ARNCLIFFE

You may wish to refer to drawings for the numbered Locations in Journal **10**.

The Walk across the Vale of Mowbray uses footpaths, green lanes (the tread of walkers' boots has sometimes made them more mud-brown than green), farm tracks, and roads. For most of the way the Route is well signed. Our simplified instructions refer to place-names you can find on maps.

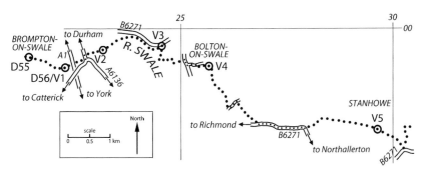

Brompton-on-Swale to Stanhowe.

*From Catterick Bridge walk along the north side of the River Swale. In ¼ km you come to some lakes in pits that were worked for river gravels in the terrace (Fig. **V2**).*

Continue along the riverside path on the level surface marking the bottom of pits into the terrace. The road 200 metres to your left is on the top surface of the terrace.

*Where the river begins to bend right, the footpath climbs from the river level to the road (Fig. **V3**). (The Route here is subject to changes due to development of new gravel pits.) Turn right on Back Lane, then left on Flat Lane.*

Loc. **V3**, SE 246 996, Flat Lane, near Bolton-on-Swale. About here the bedrock changes from Permian to Triassic (nothing is visible on the surface). For a comment on this important boundary see Journal **11** at Ingleby Arncliffe.

*Continue along Flat Lane to Bolton-on-Swale. At the B6271 turn right for 100 metres, then left on the road past the church. Just before the road crosses a bridge, go through a wicket gate on the right to a footpath beside Bolton Beck. The beck follows the boundary between the river terrace and the till plain (Fig. **V4**).*

*Continue on the beckside path till it reaches a minor road, where you turn left. After 200 metres, turn right on a track past the cottages on Ellerton Hill. Turn left on the main road for 1 km, past Kiplin Hall. Where the road bends sharp right, go straight ahead into a track past Ladybank House. At the end of the wood, take the footpath half-right, past the ruined Stanhowe Cottages (Fig. **V5** is here).*

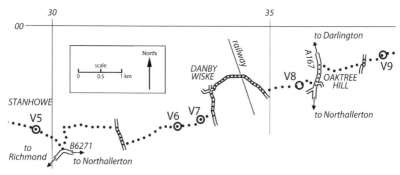

Stanhowe to Oaktree Hill.

*At the point where the path emerges onto the main road, turn left on a wide track to Moor House. Turn right past the farm and walk by fields to the next road at Brockholme. Turn right on the road for 400 metres, then left on a track towards High Brockholme. Where the track turns right, go straight ahead by footpaths and a green lane (Figs. **V6, 7**) to the next road, where you turn left into Danby Wiske.*

*Leave Danby Wiske by the road to the northeast, crossing the River Wiske and the railway line from London to Edinburgh, and ¾ km beyond the railway bridge, near the brow of the hill, take the footpath to the left. This leads to the A167 road at Oaktree Hill, where you turn left. (Fig. **V8** is about here.)*

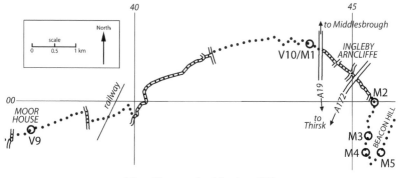

Moor House to Ingleby Arncliffe.

*Walk north along the A167 for ½ km, then take a footpath to the right into a broad green lane. After 200 metres fork left on a footpath past White House Farm. At the next road turn left, and after 150 metres right into a track to (another) Moor House (Fig. **V9**). Bear left on the footpath past the farm and continue past Northfields to a minor road, where you turn right for 300 metres. A track to the left past Wray House leads to a railway crossing.*

*From the railway crossing, walk across a small field, over a brook, and stay on the left side of the next field, at first eastwards, and then south, to Low Moor Lane. Walk along the lane, past Harlsey Grove, till it joins a tarmac road. At the road junction, go straight on into the track past Sydal Lodge (Fig. **V10**), then straight again on a footpath across fields. Cross a small brook and soon join a track which zig-zags past Longlands and Grinkle Carr to the busy A19.*

Loc. **V10/M1**, about NZ 440 013, near Grinkle Carr. Yet another hidden boundary – between the Triassic and the Jurassic. In our Walk across the Vale of Mowbray the bedrock has got progressively younger, from 300 million years old at Catterick to 200 million years old here. During that time Britain and Europe drifted slowly northwards, from the arid tropics to sub-tropical and temperate latitudes. The scenery changed from a desert in the Permo-Triassic to a warm and moderately deep sea in the early part of the Jurassic.

From here to the east coast we walk over rocks of Jurassic age.

Cross the A19, and walk on by a minor road to Ingleby Arncliffe.

JOURNAL 11 – INGLEBY ARNCLIFFE

ECONOMIC RESOURCES OF THE RIVER SWALE (Locs *V2*, *V3*)

The river terrace near Catterick and Bolton-on-Swale is up to 1½ km wide and the gravels are about 6 metres thick. In the first 6 km of the Vale we crossed over some 20 million cubic metres of gravel (some of it has been commercially extracted), and that's only a small fraction of the total amount of gravel along the river's course through the Vale of Mowbray.

This volume of gravel gives an idea of how much rock material the River Swale has eroded and transported since the end of the Ice Age. The river manages to combine scenic beauty with a load of hard work. But as we have seen earlier, it's a fierce beauty when it's in flood.

THE GREAT DYING (Loc. *V3*)

The (unseen) bedrock of the Vale of Mowbray is the Permian and Triassic. The boundary between them (which is also the boundary between the Palaeozoic and Mesozoic Eras) is covered by superficial sediments. Globally the boundary is highly significant. A catastrophic environmental event 252 million years ago brought about the Great Dying, when 95% of marine species and 70% of land species became extinct. The causes are debated – meteorite impact, eruption of a supervolcano, runaway greenhouse effect are all possibles.

This is one situation where the cover of superficial rocks makes little difference to our ability to see the evidence in the bedrock. Britain at the time was in tropical latitudes and covered by desert, so there were few plants or animals to survive or to die in the catastrophe. We can only mourn the passing of one great ecosystem (the Palaeozoic – the older era of life), welcome the one that was to come (the Mesozoic – the middle era of life), and walk on.

INTRODUCTION TO THE NORTH YORK MOORS AND THE JURASSIC SYSTEM

> Age range: 200-146 million years ago
>
> Latitude: 35° to 40° north
>
> Climate: warm temperate, like the present-day Mediterranean

The final section of the Walk, ending at Robin Hood's Bay, crosses the North York Moors and the rocks of the Jurassic system. Two hundred million years ago this part of Britain was a broad low-lying area known as the Cleveland Basin. It was bounded to the west and north by the eroding Variscan and Caledonian mountain chains of the Pennines and Southern Uplands.

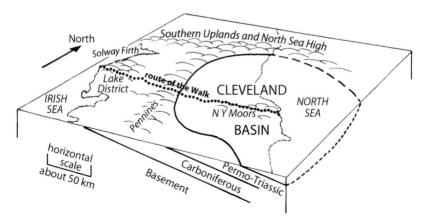

Northern England and the location of the Cleveland Basin.

During the Lower Jurassic the Basin was an extension of the early North Sea, and gradually filled with muddy sediments. In the Middle Jurassic the Basin became a broad coastal plain with big rivers depositing sands. We do not see anything of the Upper Jurassic on the Walk, but the Cleveland Basin continued to fill with sediments up to the end of the Jurassic.

Centuries of fossil-collecting, especially from the coastal exposures of the Jurassic of North Yorkshire, have produced a rich and varied haul of beautifully preserved animals and plants, which can be seen in museums all over the country. On a short visit, fossils are hard to find, but we will point out Locations where it is worth searching. We illustrate a few of the commoner types of fossil.

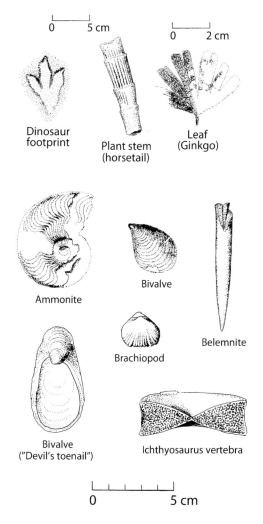

0   5 cm

0   2 cm

Dinosaur footprint

Plant stem (horsetail)

Leaf (Ginkgo)

Some types of fossil that you might find in Jurassic sandstones.

Ammonite

Bivalve

Brachiopod

Belemnite

Bivalve ("Devil's toenail")

Ichthyosaurus vertebra

*Some fossils from Jurassic mudstones. Abraded or broken pieces of the more robust fossils – **ammonites**, **belemnites**, "devil's toenails", and reptile (including dinosaur) bones – might also be found in boulder clay.*

0   5 cm

211

Though fossils may seem scarce, the warm sub-tropical Jurassic sea and land were as rich in life as the Mediterranean region is today. Reptiles, fish, and invertebrates lived in the seas; the land was well covered with vegetation, and occupied by the complete food-chain from producers and consumers to predators and scavengers; the air was filled with flying creatures. It was, apart from the risk of meeting a hungry carnivore, a pleasant place to live.

The influence of the Ice Age is as evident in the Moors as it has been in other areas and will feature at several Locations. The Jurassic bedrock of the Moors is largely covered by superficial rocks and vegetation, though there are some good inland exposures. The coast provides nearly 100% exposure of bedrock and it's worth keeping enough energy for some quality time at Robin Hood's Bay.

In the 200 metres height of Beacon Hill you climb over all the rocks you will see later in the Walk. If only they were exposed we could stop looking at the rocks when you reach the top of the hill and let you walk on in peace to Robin Hood's Bay. As it is, you may find the next drawing helpful for understanding the sequence of the rock units in the Jurassic.

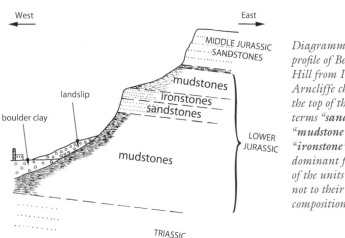

*Diagrammatic profile of Beacon Hill from Ingleby Arncliffe church to the top of the hill. The terms "**sandstone**", "**mudstone**", and "**ironstone**" refer to dominant features of the units and not to their entire compositions.*

Throughout the Moors the structure is very simple. There are few folds or faults, and the dips of the rock layers are nearly (though not quite) horizontal. You will become very familiar with the Middle Jurassic sandstones as a strong feature of the scenery. They are more resistant to erosion than the underlying rocks, so they make nearly all the high ground in the Moors. As a simple guide to the scenery of the Walk – if you are on a high ridge or plateau you are on the sandstones of the Middle Jurassic; if you are on lower ground they form the skyline. Heather moorland is an important environment and ecosystem, globally rare, but here plentiful. It covers most of the plateau of sandstone bedrock - an area of about 1400 square kilometres.

6. THE NORTH YORK MOORS

The bedrock is Jurassic in age, largely mudstones and sandstones, containing a subtle story of a change of sea level and its possible cause. The Cleveland Dyke is evidence of yet another episode in the pattern of plate movements that affected Britain. The scenery is of ridges, moors, and valleys carved by glaciers and rivers.

THE WALK – INGLEBY ARNCLIFFE TO LORD STONES

From Ingleby Arncliffe take the road to the southeast, crossing the busy A172. Continue uphill past the church and make a short stop where the track turns right (1 km from Ingleby Arncliffe).

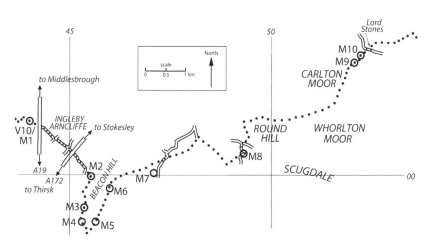

Ingleby Arncliffe to Lord Stones.

Heather

BEACON HILL

Loc. **M2**, NZ 455 000, a low bank at the foot of the main escarpment.

The small exposure shows loose sand with sandstone pebbles and boulders. This is the product of a landslide, derived from the Jurassic rocks in the slopes above.

*Fig. **M2**. The angular shapes of the rock fragments show that they have travelled only a short distance. The shapes are sharply contrasted with the rounded boulders you have seen earlier which were carried by ice or in streams.*

The hummocky ground on the gentle slopes below you marks the shape of the toe of the landslide as it spread onto the low-lying ground. The well-established vegetation there, and on the hill-slopes above, shows that the landslide occurred long before the development of the soil and trees.

*Stay on the forest track as it climbs through the wood. At the edge of the wood at SE 454 986 the track joins the Cleveland Way and doubles back to the northeast. The total distance to Loc. **M6** at the top of the hill is 2 km. On the way there are various scrappy exposures in the cuttings beside the track. You may like to look at some of these as the first Jurassic rocks you see on the Walk (but you will see better later); three specific examples follow:*

Loc. **M3**, SE 453 992, on the left side of the track.

Loc. **M4**, SE 453 989, a low escarpment about 3 metres above the track.

*Fig. **M3**. A low exposure of grey mudstones beside the track in Arncliffe Wood, partly covered by a small-scale scree of mudstone fragments.*

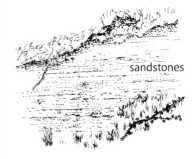

*Fig. **M4**. An exposure of white sandstones in an overgrown bank above the track in Arncliffe Wood.*

Loc. **M5**, SE 457 989. Three overgrown quarries in Middle Jurassic sandstones. This is most likely the stone that was used for building Mount Grace Priory, at the foot of the escarpment below you.

Mount Grace Priory.

RETROSPECTIVE VIEW TO THE PENNINES

When you reach the top of the ridge and can see over the trees you get fine views to the west and an opportunity to reflect on the country you have walked over for the last 60 km. The grassy platform on the left side of the track at Loc. **M5** is as good as any. The nearly flat Vale of Mowbray is covered with superficial deposits over the bedrock of Permo-Triassic, and earliest Jurassic sediments. The older Carboniferous rocks form the Pennines beyond.

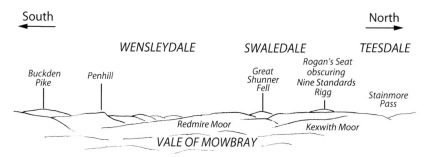

*Fig. **M5**. View west (vertically exaggerated) from the top of Beacon Hill. The Coast-to-Coast Route came along the length of Swaledale from Nine Standards Rigg.*

Continue along the path for ¾ km, past the telecommunications enclosure.

ADVANCE VIEW OF THE NORTH YORK MOORS

Loc. **M6**, SE 460 997, at the trig. point for the top of Beacon Hill, gives a good view of the next stage of the Walk. For much of the next 25 km the Route marches along the crest of the escarpment made by the resistant sandstones of the Middle Jurassic.

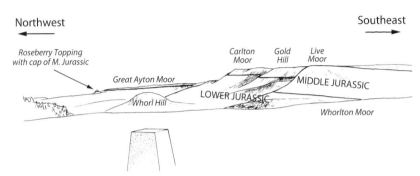

Northwest   Southeast

*Fig. **M6**. The mudstones of the Lower Jurassic form the low-lying agricultural scenery to the north and west. The sandstones of the Middle Jurassic underlie the heather moorland of the North York Moors.*

Walk on for 1¼ km across Scarth Wood Moor to Scarth Nick. Stretches of the path are paved with sandstone flags. These are not local, but Carboniferous rocks imported from dismantled mills in Lancashire or the West Riding of Yorkshire.

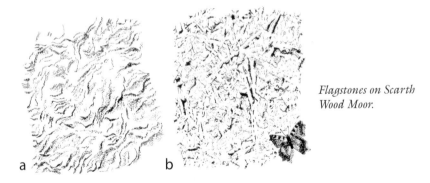

Flagstones on Scarth Wood Moor.

The top surfaces of two of the flagstones on the path across Scarth Wood Moor:

a   a flagstone with complex ripple marks;

b   a flagstone entirely covered with **trace fossils** – hundreds of burrowing trails left by animals which have not been preserved as **body fossils** in the sediment.

Stop at the signpost at the top of the steep slope (NZ 471 003) where the path turns right and goes down to the road in Scarth Nick.

A SHORT STORY OF GLACIERS AND LAKES

A small diversion can be made here, but read on – the description of the location and Figs *M7/1* and *M7/2* may tell you enough of the story without the need for the diversion.

Take the grassy track to the south and follow it for 200 metres to the top of the low hill (spot height 258 metres on the O.S. map).

Loc. **M7**, NZ 471 000. Rounded white pebbles are scattered on the top of the hill.

Fig. M7/1. The pebbles are clearly out of place in relation to present-day stream patterns. They were deposited by a short-lived torrent at the end of the last Ice Age.

The valley on the far side of the ridge east of where you are standing was a temporary lake ("Lake Scugdale") dammed by ice across the north side of the dale (Fig. **M7/2**). Loc. **M7** provides a small piece of the evidence for this history.

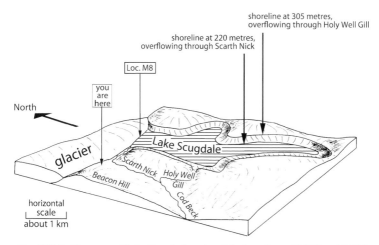

Fig. M7/2. Cartoon of Lake Scugdale as it might have been 12,000 to 10,000 years ago when Scarth Nick was being eroded. The glacier had retreated so as to expose an outflow for the lake at its northwest corner, suddenly draining a large volume of water along the edge of the glacier and eroding Scarth Nick. You will see the valley of Scugdale at the next Location, 2 km further on.

Use the smaller path beside the wall down to the road in Scarth Nick. On the opposite side of the road go through a gate to the wide track through Clain Wood. After 300 metres take a footpath steeply down to the left. Where the path meets a minor road, cross it, turning half-right, and stay on the footpath along the edge of the wood. At a stile bear left across a field to a minor road and ford.

This section of the Walk takes us through picturesque woodland and open meadows. But have in mind that only 12,000 years ago where you are walking was covered by ice at least 100 metres thick, and the higher ground above the ice was bare rock. When the ice melted the ground you are walking on would have been a slush of boulder clay. All the soil and vegetation have developed in the last 10,000 years.

Loc. **M8**, near NZ 493 005, with a view up Scugdale.

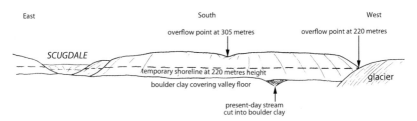

*Fig. **M8**. A wide view of Scugdale, combining features of the Ice Age with the present-day scene.*

During the Ice Age the edge of a lowland glacier was about where you are standing (see Fig. **M7/2**). A lake filled Scugdale to the height of the overflow point at the top of the ridge on the right (305 metres). As the climate warmed the glacier retreated and opened a new overflow point along the edge of the escarpment (220 metres) – think of the erosive power of a volume of water half the size of the valley of Scugdale being made suddenly available! The boulder clay in the foreground comes from an earlier stage when a glacier filled all of the valley.

The next Location is 4½ km ahead. Stay on the road to Huthwaite Green, and then straight on to a path along the edge of a plantation. Shortly after some prominent waste heaps (mudstones with a few ammonites and bivalves) and at the corner of the wood, turn right across a stile and up the steps to the open moorland of Round Hill. Continue along the escarpment of the Middle Jurassic sandstones to the top of Carlton Moor, with impressive views to the north Pennines and Teesside.

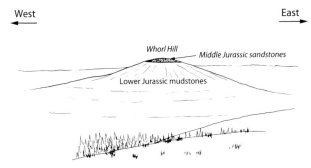

West ←   *East* →

Whorl Hill, shown without the trees. The hill is detached from the escarpment, just like Roseberry Topping (Fig. M6), and is made of the same Jurassic rocks, (no, it's not a volcano!). The thin cap of sandstones protects the softer mudstones from erosion, but once it's worn away the hill will rather quickly, in geological terms, be reduced to the level of the surrounding plain.

MIDDLE JURASSIC SANDSTONES

Loc. **M9**, NZ 520 027, 100 metres east of the summit of Carlton Moor, where a quarry below the path comes into view.

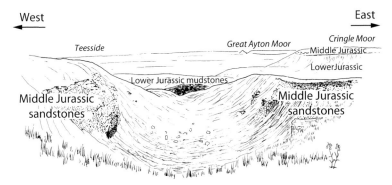

*Fig. **M9**. The quarry was worked for the Middle Jurassic sandstones. Beyond and below the quarry is a second quarry in mudstones at the top of the Lower Jurassic. In the distance, on Cringle Moor, the same sandstones and mudstones make the well-defined crags near the top of the moor. You may be able to make out the same boundary on Great Ayton Moor in the far distance. For a comment see the next Location and Journal 12.*

Continue for 200 metres on the paved path, which zig-zags down the steepest part of the escarpment made by the thick sandstone. Stop briefly at the second sharp right corner.

Loc. **M10**, NZ 522 028. You are here at the level of the base of the sandstones.

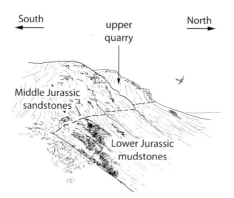

Fig. M10. The lower quarry on Carlton Moor. The boundary between the Lower and Middle Jurassic is obscured by vegetation, but can be placed to within a metre. The quarry was worked for mudstones to make alum (Journal 12)

The sudden change from mudstones to sandstones implies a significant change of environment. This is explained in the Journal.

Continue down the path to the road and turn right (½ km). Lord Stones Café is on the left.

JOURNAL 12 – LORD STONES

THE ENVIRONMENTAL CHANGE IN THE JURASSIC (Loc. *M10*).

The mudstones at Loc. **M10** were deposited in the sea, perhaps a hundred metres or so deep. (To get a feeling for how deep this is, think back to Scugdale, and the lake that filled it to a similar depth.) Waves had little effect on the sea floor, which would have been for the most part stagnant and lifeless. The few fossils are the remains of animals that lived in the oxygenated surface waters of the sea.

The thick sandstones overlying the mudstones were deposited in large rivers, which we will see later were part of an extensive coastal plain or deltaic system.

The change from deep sea to land with rivers, over a vertical distance of a metre or less, must have been the result of a change of sea level by at least 100 metres, combined with the arrival of vast quantities of sandy sediment. If the contact between the mudstones and the sandstones were better exposed, one would look for solid evidence about how this happened.

We have seen sudden changes of environment before – in the Yoredale sequences of the Carboniferous, for instance (Journal 7). There the switch from one cycle to the next was the result of a change from land to sea. Here it is the other way round, so there is a different kind of explanation. (Like movements in human history it's often the sudden changes, and their causes, which are more interesting than the long periods of stability.)

From exposures elsewhere in the Moors, we know that there was a widespread episode of gentle folding, followed by erosion of the Lower Jurassic, before the arrival of the Middle Jurassic sandstones. The boundary between the mudstones and the sandstones is in fact an **unconformity**, though on a smaller scale than unconformities we have seen earlier. At the same time, and probably related, there was uplift and the development of a big volcano in the central North Sea, 400 km to the NNE. The drawing shows the change in environment that resulted.

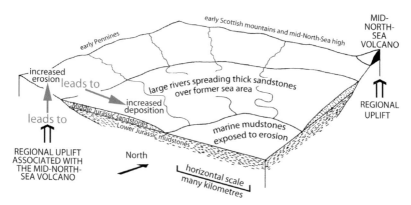

Uplift of the central North Sea and the Cleveland Basin caused profound changes in the geography of the area.

Although the unconformity here may appear relatively trivial, it is part of the evidence for crustal movements of much wider significance – in this instance in the history of the North Sea as a major sedimentary basin.

ALUM – AN EARLY CHEMICAL INDUSTRY (Loc. M10).

The lower quarry on Carlton Bank was worked for a part of the Lower Jurassic mudstones with the right proportion of clay minerals (aluminium silicates) and pyrite (iron sulphide) to manufacture alum (aluminium sulphate, with potassium or ammonium sulphate).

The process was complex, requiring roasting (calcination) of the mudstone for up to a year, followed by repeated washing (leaching) to extract the aluminium sulphate. Chemical treatment with calcined seaweed or with human urine, followed by evaporation, produced the alum crystals.

The industry was widespread in the North York Moors in the seventeenth to nineteenth centuries when alum was an essential ingredient for dyeing wool. In most places distinctive brick-coloured burnt mudstones are all that is left to mark the locations of the former alum works. The fascinating history of the rise and decline of the alum industry is described in several books and leaflets.

THE WALK – LORD STONES
TO BLAKEY RIDGE

Leave Lord Stones Café through the car park to the north, and follow the path to the right to the top of Cringle Moor (1 km).

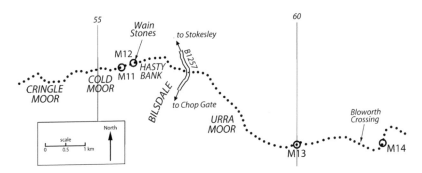

Cringle Moor to Bloworth Crossing.

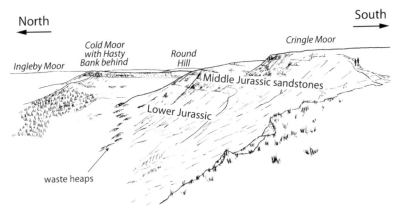

View east from the top of Cringle Moor. The Route ahead continues over the nearer moors and then over Round Hill in the distance.

The waste heaps at the bottom of the Moor are the product of mining for jet – fossilised wood from monkey-puzzle trees in the Jurassic, much used as an easily carved and polished semi-precious stone, fashionable in Victorian times.

The next Location is 2 km ahead. Continue on the path along the top of Cringle Moor and across Cold Moor. Between Cringle and Cold Moors there is a prominent heap of burned red clay marking the site of a former alum works. All along the crest of the Moors there are extensive views to the north and the industrial area of Teesside. Its location is historically due in part to the former mineral resources of the North York Moors.

West ←

East →

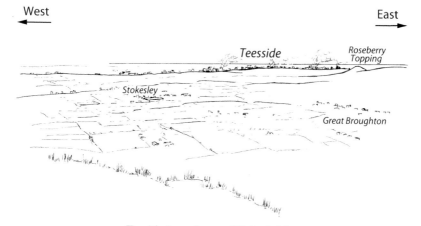

Teesside from the top of Cringle Moor.

EARLY STREET ART

Loc. **M11**, NZ 556 035. In the col between Cold Moor and the Wain Stones several of the large sandstone slabs show prehistoric rock art – patterns inscribed in the late Neolithic to early Bronze Age, 5000 to 4000 years ago. One of the carved stones is easily accessible only a few steps off the Route. From the gate at the lowest point, walk to the large stone on the near skyline 20 metres to the southeast.

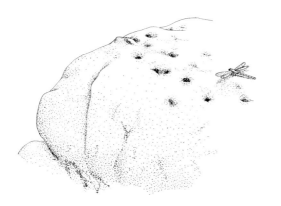

*Fig. **M11**. Rock art on a corner of the large slab of sandstone. There are several cups 4-5 cm across and a runnel down the side of the stone. Sometimes the man-made marks are hard to distinguish from natural weathering.*

On the way up to the Wain Stones there are waste heaps from the jet-mining in the Lower Jurassic mudstones.

THE MIDDLE JURASSIC SANDSTONES AGAIN

Loc. **M12**, NZ 559 036, on the path at the base of the Wain Stones (a popular site for rock-climbing).

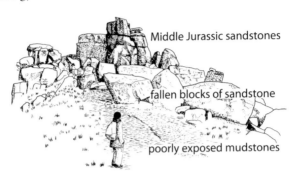

Middle Jurassic sandstones

fallen blocks of sandstone

poorly exposed mudstones

Fig. M12. Wain Stones. The top of the exposure is thick sandstones of the Middle Jurassic. Below are shallow-water mudstones, also in the Middle Jurassic – a unit which was missing at Carlton Moor and further evidence for the unconformity (Journal 12).

From the Wain Stones walk along the top of Hasty Bank and down the path into Bilsdale – total distance 2 km. Near the base of the escarpment you pass extensive waste heaps, which can be searched for ammonites and bivalves, though the fossils are not common.

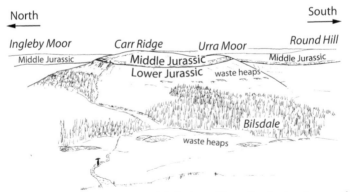

North ◄——— South ———►

Ingleby Moor Carr Ridge Urra Moor Round Hill
Middle Jurassic Middle Jurassic Middle Jurassic
Lower Jurassic waste heaps

Bilsdale

waste heaps

The view looking east across Bilsdale from Hasty Bank, showing gentle folding of the Middle Jurassic sandstones. The waste heaps on both sides of the dale map out the level in the mudstones which was worked for jet.

The next Location is 4 km from the head of Bilsdale. Walk up the well-marked path to Urra Moor. For the first ½ km the path rises steeply through the thick sandstones at the base of the Middle Jurassic. At the top of Carr Ridge a layer of mudstones within the sandstone provides flatter walking for 1 km. A rise through more sandstones leads to Round Hill.

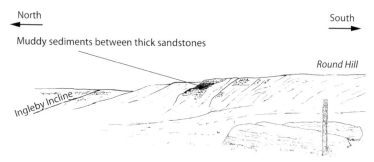

Distant view of the Middle Jurassic escarpment from Carr Ridge. Ingleby Incline was part of the railway system connecting iron-mines in the Moors with Teesside.

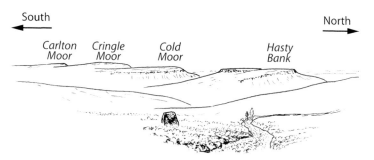

View from Round Hill back to the west. The Middle Jurassic sandstones cap the hills.

FORMATION OF THE PRESENT-DAY SOIL

Loc. **M13**, NZ 600 015, a small pond on the south side of the track.

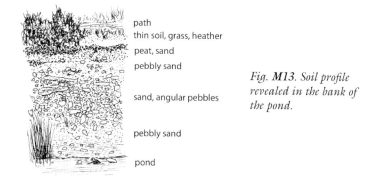

path
thin soil, grass, heather
peat, sand
pebbly sand

sand, angular pebbles

pebbly sand

pond

Fig. M13. Soil profile revealed in the bank of the pond.

Although not covered by ice during the last glaciation the exposed Jurassic sandstones would have been permanently frozen, and further broken up by soil formation in the last 12,000 years. The peat has grown since the soil first formed.

INDUSTRY IN AN IDYLLIC LANDSCAPE

Continue for 1½ km along the path to Bloworth Crossing, where you join the track of the old railway. To the northwest it links to the head of Ingleby Incline where trucks were lowered to the base of the escarpment and from there to the industrial centre of Teesside. Ahead the track leads by sweeping curves to Blakey Ridge (a further 8 km), and thence to the former ironstone mines in Rosedale.

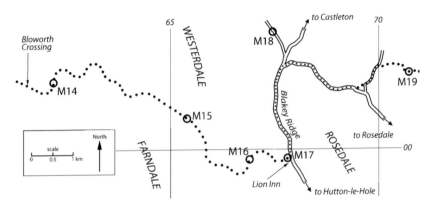

Bloworth Crossing to Rosedale.

We have already seen some of the industrial heritage of the North York Moors in the waste material from jet-mining and alum-working. As we continue eastwards the significance and variety of former mineral industries increases. At this point the railway is the only obvious link with the past. Until it closed in 1929 it must have made an incongruous contrast with the surrounding remote and peaceful moorland and the agricultural dales. Now the easy walking on its track bed allows more time to enjoy the scenery.

Loc. **M14**, NZ 622 015, at any point where you can look southeast down Farndale.

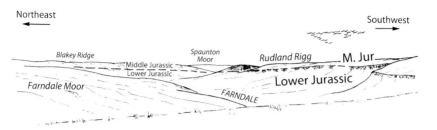

Fig. M14. The scars at the top of the west side of the dale are nearly horizontal, but in the distance on Rudland Rigg they dip gently to the south. Spaunton Moor in the far distance is near the south edge of the Moors; the rocks there are at the top of the Middle Jurassic, about 150 metres higher in the sequence than the rocks we are standing on.

Walk on another 4 km. The track is surfaced with rock and cinders, and occasional pieces of steel-making slag (heavy, black, sometimes with one shiny glassy surface), used refractory bricks (mottled grey/yellow, with black coating of slag), and pieces of scrap iron. The next Location is at the end of a 1 km straight section of the track.

THE CLEVELAND ANTICLINE, A GAS FIELD, AND THE RIVER SYSTEM – A ONE-STOP SHOP AT A GOOD VIEWPOINT

Loc. **M15**, NZ 654 007, on Farndale Moor, at the signpost for the bridleway (the Esk Valley Way) from Farndale to Castleton.

From this location you can look south into Farndale and north into Westerdale. You are standing exactly on the watershed between the southward dales, taking streams to the Vale of Pickering and the Humber, and the northward dales, draining to Eskdale and the sea at Whitby.

The poorly exposed scars towards the top of the valley sides are outcrops of the familiar resistant Middle Jurassic sandstones. The strata are horizontal or gently undulating, but in the distance to both north and south the heights of the scars are about 50 metres lower than they are closer to you. In the far distance in both dales the Middle Jurassic sandstones dip under rocks at higher levels of the Middle Jurassic.

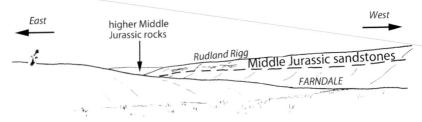

Fig. *M15/1*. *View south into Farndale from the old railway track, with gently south-dipping Middle Jurassic sandstones.*

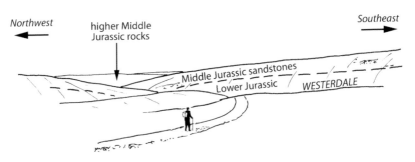

Fig. *M15/2*. *View north into Westerdale from the same point, with north-dipping Jurassic rocks.*

The simple observation that the Jurassic rocks dip in opposite directions on each side of the Route has several consequences. Journal **13** provides detail.

> *Continue for 2½ km along the old railway track until the Lion Inn comes into view on Blakey Ridge. Look for a view into Farndale like the one shown in Fig. **M16**.*

LANDSLIDES

Loc. **M16**, SE 669 998 or thereabouts. **Landslides** on the east side of Farndale form a sequence of parallel ridges below the escarpment of the Middle Jurassic sandstones. It looks as though each ridge was detached from the full length of the escarpment and slipped over the mudstones below, creating the effect of a slow-moving procession.

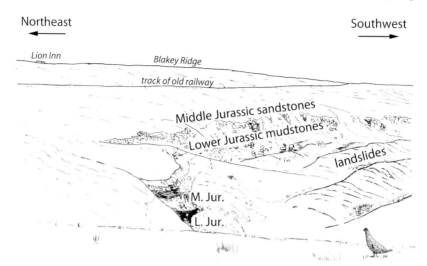

Fig. M16. The east side of Farndale from the old railway track. The base of the Middle Jurassic sandstones is about at the bottom of the crags of the escarpment.

At the same Location, looking behind you, the rough ground beside the track on the uphill side is the result of digging into the hillside for a thin seam of coal within the Middle Jurassic.

Continue on the old railway track to SE 675 998 and then left to Blakey Ridge (1 km).

EARLY COAL-MINING...

Loc. **M17**, SE 678 998, Blakey Howe or Cockpit Hill, 100 metres north of the Lion Inn. An alternative method of working a near-surface coal seam (the same one as at Loc. **M16**) was to dig vertically down, forming a bell pit. (Alfred Wainwright records that cockfights used to be held in the bowl that remains.) An open bell pit will be seen a few kilometres further on.

... AND EARLY IRON-MAKING

From Loc. **M17** looking east there is a good view of Rosedale.

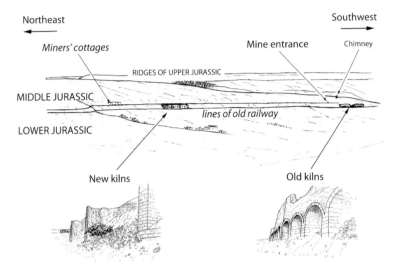

Fig. M17. The east side of Rosedale from Blakey Ridge, showing some of the constructions from the Victorian iron-making industry. The modern white concrete pyramid of Fylingdales radar station is on the extreme left below the furthest ridge.

JOURNAL 13 – BLAKEY RIDGE

Lion Inn.

THE MIDDLE JURASSIC SANDSTONES (Loc. *M12*).

The picture to have in mind for the Middle Jurassic is that at this time the Cleveland Basin was a wide coastal plain. The sea was several tens of kilometres to the east. The thick sandstones were deposited in the channels of large rivers – much bigger than the present-day rivers of the North York Moors. Between the channels finer sediments were deposited on the adjacent floodplains, which were richly covered with vegetation.

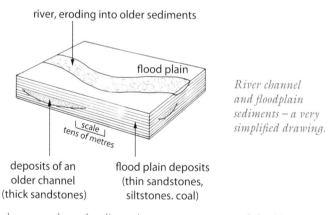

River channel and floodplain sediments – a very simplified drawing.

The rocks exposed on the discontinuous escarpments of the Moors are nearly all thick channel sandstones, suggesting that the thinner and softer floodplain sediments have been eroded from the areas between.

THE CLEVELAND ANTICLINE (Loc. *M15*).

The height differences of the scars and the opposite directions of dip of the Jurassic rocks in Farndale and Westerdale might seem too small to be significant. But they mark two important features – the crest of the major arch-shaped fold known as the Cleveland **Anticline**, and the watershed of the North York Moors.

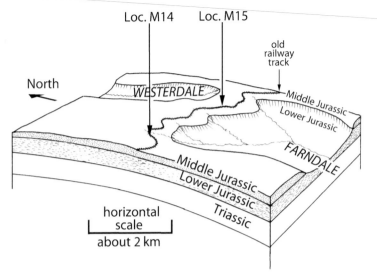

Cartoon showing the surface topography and the outcrop of the Middle Jurassic sandstones around the heads of Westerdale and Farndale.

The gentle dips that you saw in the outcrops are continued in the older layers below ground. They define a broad arch with its crest running west to east. The crest of the fold makes a series of undulating, sinuous (sensuous?) curves from west to east:

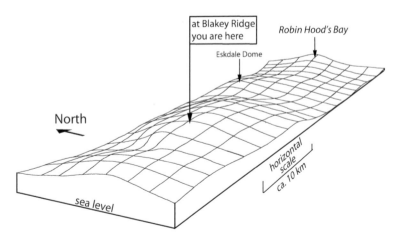

The Cleveland Anticline, from Farndale Moor to Robin Hood's Bay, showing the shape of the top of the Lower Jurassic with the younger layers peeled off. The lines are at 2 km intervals. This way of representing a structure is used for finding places where oil and gas could have collected (see opposite).

The Cleveland Anticline runs almost the whole west-to-east length of the North York Moors. Early in its existence it would have formed an impressive ridge rising to at least 1000 metres (now it is 450 metres at the highest point). Erosion has stripped the younger layers of Upper Jurassic from the crest of the ridge while retaining them on the flanks. Valleys like Westerdale and Farndale have eaten into the flanks of the ridge to reveal the older layers of Lower Jurassic.

OIL AND GAS (Loc. M15).

Gas comes from the decay of fossil plants in terrestrial sediments like the Carboniferous Coal Measures. Oil comes from marine sediments, like those in the Lower Jurassic, as a product of decay of animal bodies. Oil and gas are both less dense than water, and migrate upwards through permeable rock layers until they meet an impermeable barrier. Any geological structure that prevents upward migration creates a trap and a potential hydrocarbon reservoir. Gently folded layers of permeable and impermeable rocks in the form of an arch or dome are the simplest of the many possible types of trap. As the drawing shows, the Cleveland Anticline is one of these.

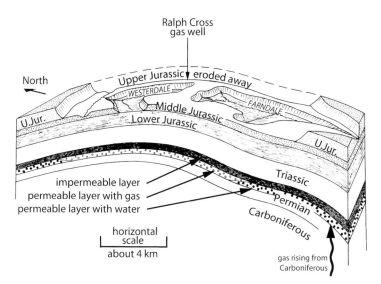

The surface topography and below-ground structure of Westerdale and Farndale (a wider view than the previous cartoon).

One of the high points on the anticline was drilled in 1966 at Loc. **M18** near Ralphs Cross, 3 km ahead on the walk. A small accumulation of gas was found in Permian rocks at a depth of 1040 metres. Similar gas- and oil-bearing structures occur elsewhere in northern England. In the 1960s Whitby was the first town in Britain to be supplied with natural gas – from the Eskdale Dome, further east along the Cleveland Anticline. Much larger reservoirs occur below the North Sea. Such structures are also of interest at the present day for the storage of gas or for the disposal of carbon dioxide.

Oil or gas still held in the source rocks, especially in the Carboniferous and the Jurassic, are of current interest as a source of energy and as a chemical resource. The debate on hydraulic fracturing ("fracking") relates to the methods of extracting the hydrocarbons from such rocks.

THE DRAINAGE PATTERN OF THE NORTH YORK MOORS (Loc. M15).

An episode of mountain-building 65 million years ago created the Alps of southern Europe. Northern England, 1200 km to the northwest, felt only very gentle folding. The Cleveland Basin maintained its identity, but was inverted (in effect, turned inside out) to form the Cleveland Anticline. Streams ran off the long whaleback ridge and developed into the pattern of north- and south-draining valleys that we see today. The present-day watershed of the Moors nearly coincides with the crest of the Cleveland Anticline.

COAL IN THE JURASSIC (Loc. M16).

Poor-quality coal was mined from a layer within the sandstones of the Middle Jurassic. The seam was up to 60 cm thick and can be mapped discontinuously over an area of about 250 square km, mostly to the southwest from Blakey Ridge. The outcrops are near the tops of the moors and much of the coal seam had been eroded away long before mining started.

The coal was worked by shallow mines, either by horizontal adits or by bell pits (to be seen at Loc. **M19**). This Jurassic coal was worked for local use until the mid-nineteenth century when the coming of the railway brought in better-quality Carboniferous coal from the County Durham coalfields.

Making reasonable assumptions about how vegetable matter is converted into coal, the seam would have formed from a layer of peat about 6 metres thick, accumulated over several thousand years. The peat must have been protected from oxidation by a high local water table, so this area was most likely a swamp in the floodplain of a river. (When we burn coal we are adding the oxygen it was deprived of in its formation, and converting it to carbon dioxide to add to the present-day atmosphere.) Subsidence and sedimentation continued to a depth of hundreds of metres, and the peat was compressed and water driven out to convert it into the layer of coal.

ROSEDALE AS A FORMER INDUSTRIAL CENTRE (Loc. M17).

Iron was worked in Rosedale from Mediaeval times, using low-grade silicate ores with up to about 30% iron. Larger-scale production started in 1853 with the discovery of a small seam of magnetite (iron oxide) ore, containing about 60% metallic iron, at the base of the Middle Jurassic. The railway was constructed in 1861 to take the ore to furnaces in Teesside and County Durham. Extraction of iron ore continued until the 1920s, when the mines closed due to exhaustion, the increasing scale of production elsewhere, and competition from rich imported ores.

There were numerous other industries based on geological resources – coal, building stone, clay for brick-making, jet, sand for glass-making – and the population who depended on these industries for their living. Rosedale in the nineteenth century was as much an industrial centre as it is now an idyllic rural scene. Mines, shafts, kilns, chimneys, rail- and tramways, inclines, tracks, as well as houses and cottages were constructed, particularly around the central part of the dale at Rosedale Abbey. Some of the few remaining industrial buildings are shown in Fig. **M17**.

THE WALK – BLAKEY RIDGE TO GROSMONT

*From the Lion Inn walk north to the head of Blakey Ridge (2½ km). Loc. **M18** is off-piste and just for wider geographical reference.*

Loc. **M18**, NZ 674 027, is the site of a gas well 1 km NNW of the road junction at Rosedale Head. It was drilled at one of the high points on the Cleveland Anticline. The concrete base is all that's left, so it's not worth visiting, but it does mark a position on the crest of the Anticline (Journal **13**, Oil and Gas).

Continue on the Rosedale road for 2¼ km. You are walking on the watershed between the north and the south dales. Turn left on a minor road for ¾ km and stop for a moment at the gate on the right.

If the air is clear enough for long views, look north along the line of the road to see the top of a white chimney 18 km away. This is at the Boulby mine, working salt deposits in Permian rocks 1100 metres below surface. It will be referred to in the Journal at Robin Hood's Bay. The mine contains an underground science laboratory, studying, among other projects, the search for dark matter in the universe.

Go through the gate and follow the track – the Cut Road – for ¾ km, past a small shooting lodge. Stop at the second bend after the lodge.

COAL IN A BELL PIT

Loc. **M19**, NZ 707 018, 400 metres SSE of Trough House. Within the fenced-off enclosure is an open bell pit for shallow mining of coal, from the same seam as at the Lion Inn. Fragments of coal can be seen on the surrounding waste heap.

*Fig. **M19**. A bell pit in use for extracting coal.*

Continue along the track for 1 km to its lowest point, where a cairn marks a footpath to the north. The path is part of a paved trod – George Gap Causeway; the paving is preserved in a section 100 metres south of the cairn.

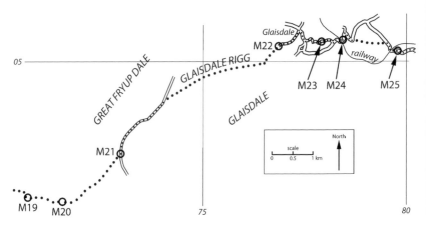

Great Fryup Dale to Glaisdale.

LANDSLIDES, ICE-AGE VALLEYS, AND IRON-MAKING

Loc. **M20**, NZ 715 017, the view to the north from the cairn.

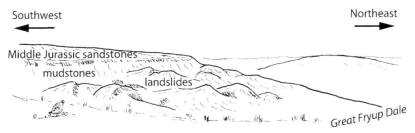

Fig. M20. Landslides cover much of the west side of Fryup Dale.
They are clearly older than streams which have eroded into them.

The irregular shapes of these landslides make a contrast with the organised pattern of those seen in Farndale (Fig. **M16**). Otherwise the situation is the same – the Middle Jurassic sandstones slipped downhill on the easily deformed mudstones beneath.

[A short walk from the cairn northwards on the footpath leads to a dramatic view of Fryup Dale and a classic exposure of the Lower and Middle Jurassic at Yew Grain Scar.]

Continue on the Cut Road for 2 km along the southeast side of Fryup Dale.

Loc. **M21**, NZ 730 028, where the track joins the tarmac road, and there is a view along the length of Glaisdale.

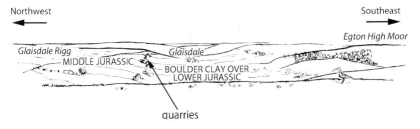

Fig. M21. Looking northeast from the head of Glaisdale. The boundary between the Lower and Middle Jurassic is below the prominent crags and quarries on the northwest side of the dale. The route of the Walk is along Glaisdale Rigg

It is 5 km to the next Location. Walk along the tarmac road, with views into Fryup Dale to the left and Glaisdale to the right. (We are now to the north of the watershed of the Moors; the streams in both dales flow northwards to join the River Esk.)

At the top of the hill, where the road bends slightly to the left, go straight ahead on the broad track. Parts of the track are surfaced with lumps of green-grey blast furnace slag (from Teesside, a by-product of iron-making).

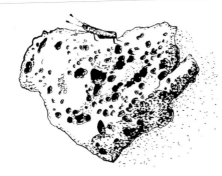

Blast furnace slag.

The holes were made by gas bubbles trapped when the molten slag solidified. In this respect it physically resembles the texture of some gassy lavas (pumice). And chemically, by a coincidence of the outcome of two very different processes, the composition of blast furnace slag is like that of some stony meteorites that represent the earliest material to have condensed from the primitive Sun's planetary nebula 4.6 billion years ago.

At NZ 765 050 the track joins, and immediately turns away from, the route of an old tramway which linked nineteenth-century iron-mines in the valley to the right with ironworks in Glaisdale village.

Loc. **M22**, NZ 768 053, at the gate, and beginning of the tarmac lane.

Until 10,000 years ago, lower Eskdale was occupied by a glacier which spread up the dale from the east. When the ice melted, erosion and deposition made changes in the scenery, best appreciated by observations from several viewpoints, starting with this one.

Fig. M22/1. Egton Banks is a ridge of boulder clay and sandy deposits formed as the glacier was melting.

When the river re-occupied the valley, ridges like Egton Banks obstructed its course, forcing a big bend to the south to find a way through.

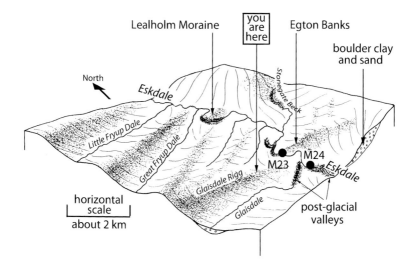

Fig. M22/2. An overview of the Esk valley. The southward bends of the river at Lealholm (barely visible from Loc. M22) and at Egton Banks were caused by ridges made across the valley as the glacier melted. The deep narrow post-glacial valleys were made by floods of meltwater at successive stages of the retreat of the ice. We will see two of them at Locs M23 and M24.

A drawing in Journal **14** at Grosmont shows the same view as it might have been towards the end of the Ice Age.

Walk on into Glaisdale (1 km). Follow the lane into the village, and turn right when it joins the bigger road. At the end of the terrace of houses on the left of the main street, turn left and follow the road down to the river.

Loc. **M23**, beside the river in Glaisdale village. There was an ironworks at Glaisdale in the third quarter of the nineteenth century, using both locally mined and imported ore.

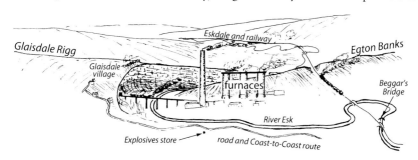

Fig. M23. An impression of the former ironworks on the inside of the bend of the River Esk around NZ 778 057.

The glacial ridge of Egton Banks diverted the river, causing it to erode into the lower end of Glaisdale Rigg behind the ironworks.

The only remaining building of the iron-mining and ironworks is the elegantly detailed explosives store standing alone in the field at NZ 779 054. The building is made of brick from another of the local industries.

The explosives store.

We shall say more about the iron-making industry when we get to Grosmont, 6 km further on, where there was another ironworks.

Walk on to rejoin the main road at Carr End, turn left, and follow the bends of the road to pass under the railway bridge (½ km).

Loc. **M24**, NZ 784 055, Beggar's Bridge (1619) over the River Esk.

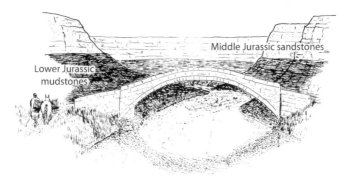

Fig. M24. A composite drawing, showing Beggar's Bridge as it might have been 400 years ago, and the gorge of the River Esk as it might have been 10,000 years ago, at the end of the Ice Age and before it was covered with vegetation. The location of the gorge is shown in Fig. M22/2.

Just before the railway bridge the usual Coast-to-Coast route takes a footpath to the right through East Arncliff Wood on the south side of the river gorge. However, it is worth making a detour (shorter than the standard route) to visit a quarry in the Cleveland Dyke. The rock is a dolerite – a common type of intrusive igneous rock. Its significance is not so much in the rock itself as in the processes it represents – nothing less than the opening of the North Atlantic Ocean. The distance from Glaisdale is 2½ km. From Beggar's Bridge continue along the tarmac road and up Limber Hill. At the sharp left bend at the top (NZ 787 055) take the footpath to the right, leading to another road at Broom House Farm (NZ 796 053). Walk downhill to the right. The quarry is 150 metres beyond the railway bridge; part of it is now a small car-parking area.

THE CLEVELAND DYKE AND THE ATLANTIC OCEAN

Loc. **M25**, NZ 797(6) 052(5), Duckscar Quarry. The quarry is well covered by trees and you need to be in the right place to get the most informative view. As you walk down the hill from the railway bridge, stop at the foot of the final slope where the road levels out close to the river. The drawing shows the bottom left corner of the quarry, closest to the road, viewed in a direction parallel to the road and looking back towards the railway bridge.

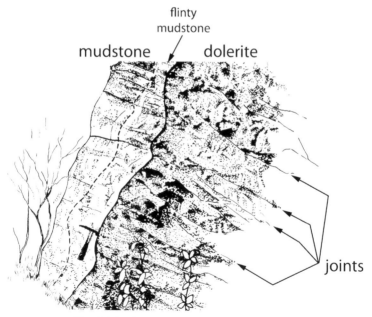

*Fig. **M25**. The wall of the quarry is **dolerite**, with a thin skin of mudstone sticking to it.*

The two rocks look surprisingly similar, as both are generally dark or rust-coloured, but the contact between them can be traced as shown in the drawing. The freshly broken dolerite is black and the mudstones are yellow-white. The dolerite **magma** was intruded at about 1200°C and its heat baked (**metamorphosed**) the mudstones into a flint-hard rock. As the magma cooled and solidified, contraction joints formed in the dolerite perpendicular to the cooling surface.

The age of the dyke is 56 million years, contemporaneous with the opening of the North Atlantic Ocean.

This small quarry is one of many, mostly much larger, which worked the very tough dolerite rock. It was widely used as roadstone, and was of such value that it was mined as well as quarried, and was not used locally for buildings or walls.

Further detail is in Journal **14**.

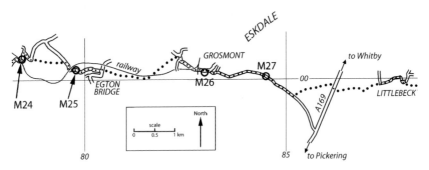

Egton Bridge to Littlebeck.

Continue along the tarmac road. At the T-junction turn left and then right into the Egton Estates road, leading to Grosmont (3½ km). The Route is beside the River Esk and for most of the way is on flat ground made by a former lake or river terrace. The slopes to the north are thickly covered by deposits left by the melting glacier which filled Eskdale until about 10,000 years ago. For much of its course the Esk cuts into superficial deposits, but occasionally it erodes into bedrock. An example can be seen from the field gate after the railway bridge at NZ 817 051 – on the far bank of the river there is a cliff of grey Jurassic mudstones.

At the end of the path turn right on the road towards Grosmont. Turn left through the car park.

Pillars which supported a conveyor belt, in the car park close to the station. This is one of the few remaining constructions of the ironworks.

Grosmont was an industrial centre in the mid- to late-nineteenth century. In addition to the ironworks there were brick kilns and alum works. The railway junction provided connections to Whitby and the sea, and inland to York and Middlesbrough.

Here you can make a short detour to see a good exposure of ironstones in the Lower Jurassic, with an opportunity to find fossils. On the far side of the railway crossing turn right across the footbridge and into the churchyard. Pass to the right of the church (a lichen-encrusted glacial erratic of Shap granite from the Lake District lies outside the west end) and then left on the grassy lane down to the river.

IRONSTONE IN THE LOWER JURASSIC

Loc. **M26**, NZ 830 052, at the bend of the Murk Esk. The cliff on the north bank of the river is Lower Jurassic mudstones with **ironstone** layers.

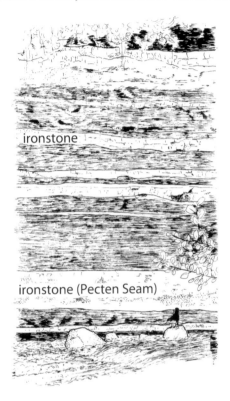

ironstone

ironstone (Pecten Seam)

*Fig. **M26/1**. Ironstones in the Lower Jurassic. The unlabelled layers are mudstones and siltstones.*

Underground workings extended below much of Grosmont village. One of the mine entrances is on the north bank of the river a few metres upstream from the view in the drawing.

On the near side of the river, under the trees beside the lane, you can see the lower of the two ironstones – the Pecten Seam, containing large single shells of that bivalve (Fig. **M26/2**). Before leaving it's worth taking a look at the shingle bank at the bend of the river, where many of the pebbles contain fossils (Fig. **M26/3**).

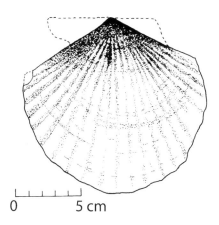

0   5 cm

*Fig. **M26/2**. A single shell of the fossil scallop Pseudopecten.*

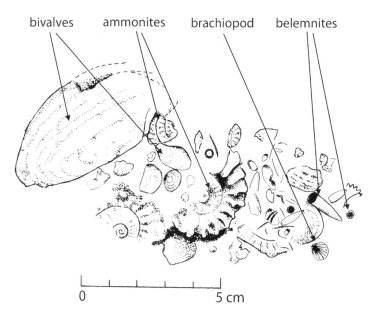

bivalves   ammonites   brachiopod   belemnites

0   5 cm

*Fig. **M26/3**. A richly shelly bed in a boulder from the Murk Esk.*

Return by the same route to Grosmont.

JOURNAL 14 – GROSMONT

ESKDALE AT THE END OF THE ICE AGE (Locs *M22-24*).

The distribution of boulder clay in and around the North York Moors shows that glaciers surrounded the area on the west, north, and east sides. The eastern part of Eskdale and its side-valleys were occupied by ice in the final glaciation of the Ice Age, but the west of the dale and the higher parts of the Moors were not covered.

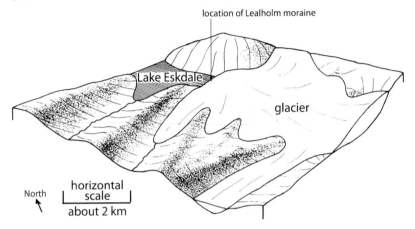

*The same area as **Fig. M22/2**, as it might have been towards the end of the Ice Age.*

Upper Eskdale was occupied by a lake, at first dammed by the glacier and then, as the ice melted, by the Lealholm moraine.

THE GLOBAL SIGNIFICANCE OF A SMALL QUARRY (Loc. *M25*).

Duckscar quarry is one small exposure of a very large igneous intrusion – the Cleveland Dyke. **Dykes** are made from **igneous** magma, most commonly **dolerite**, intruded into vertical or steeply dipping fractures to make long narrow outcrops. The Cleveland Dyke is the longest of many dykes with a generally northwest-southeast trend passing through or close to a big volcano on what is now the Island of Mull, 400 km to the northwest. The volcano was active from 62 to 55 million years ago.

Towards the ESE the dyke reaches nearly as far as the coast, coming to an end 6 km southwest of Robin Hood's Bay. It is up to 25 metres wide. Without doubt it extends downwards, perhaps as far as the **mantle**, 35-40 km below your feet, where the magma came from. It certainly extended upwards, but it's not possible to tell whether it might have reached the surface of the Earth and formed a lava flow. (If it did it would have made a spectacular fissure eruption!)

Intrusion of the dykes coincided with the opening of the North Atlantic Ocean (60 to 55 million years ago) and the splitting of the older continent of Laurasia into North America and Eurasia. The present-day continental shelf edge marks the line where the Mid-Atlantic Ridge first appeared and new **oceanic crust** started to form.

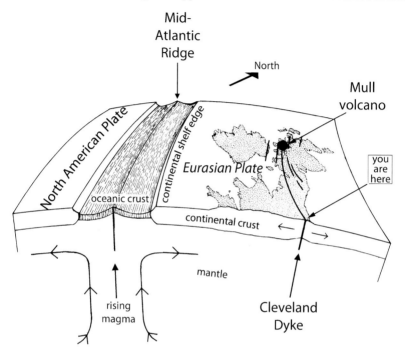

Cartoon of part of the surface of the Earth, showing Britain and the continental shelf edge as they are at the present day, combined with an early stage of development of the North Atlantic and its newly formed oceanic crust, about 50 million years ago. Only a few of the hundreds of dykes in Scotland and northern England are shown. The vertical scale is exaggerated.

The whole process was driven by convective movements in the Earth's mantle. The original Laurasian continental plate split because movements in the mantle were stretching the crust in a northeast-southwest direction. The same direction of extension made the fractures that allowed the dykes to be intruded. The heat rising with the convection produced a continuous supply of dolerite magma to make the dykes and the new oceanic crust.

A conservative guess at the volume of the entire Cleveland Dyke is 100 cubic km – a volume that would fill all of Eskdale and its side-valleys three times over. It's estimated that the Cleveland Dyke could have been intruded over a period of about five days. The opening of the fracture and the supply of such a prodigious quantity of magma in such a short time is hard to picture, but they are matched by processes at an active volcano such as Iceland, on the Mid-Atlantic Ridge. The Cleveland Dyke gives an impression of what is happening below the surface at the present day in the formation of a **constructive plate boundary** or **mid-ocean ridge**.

A final comment – the opening of the North Atlantic Ocean transferred Britain from the interior of the old Laurasia to the margin of the new Eurasian continent. The new ocean altered global patterns of circulation of sea water and the atmosphere – without the Gulf Stream and Atlantic weather systems Britain's climate would be much more continental in character. (It could even be argued that the consequences influenced modern politics and economics – think of Britain's history as a seafaring nation and its position in relation to both the United States of America and Europe, for instance.) In its quiet way this little quarry is a part of the evidence for major global changes.

IRONSTONES (Loc. M26).

The abundance of fossils in the ironstones implies that the water was warm and well oxygenated. Ironstone is deposited slowly in restricted shallow seas, with iron supplied in solution by leaching from adjacent land. The rivers had only enough energy to transport the finer muddy products of erosion into the sea. The geography of the Cleveland Basin at this time was a broad and shallow warm sea or lagoon, with low-lying land somewhere near. It's an environment for which it's hard to find a modern equivalent.

IRON ORE AND IRON-MAKING

The layers of iron ore in the Lower Jurassic were mostly less than a metre thick. The maximum iron content of the ores was around 30%. In the nineteenth century the ores were rich enough to warrant building furnaces to extract and process the iron locally.

By present-day standards, with supplies of oxide ore containing 65-70% metal available in millions of tonnes, the ironstones of the Moors are far below economic value. Developments in extraction metallurgy result in modern furnaces producing 60,000 tonnes of iron or more per week. In the nineteenth century furnaces could only produce that much iron in a year. Technological advances account both for the development of the local ironworks in Victorian times and then for their decline in favour of much larger coastal sites (such as Teesside) in modern times.

THE WALK – GROSMONT
TO ROBIN HOOD'S BAY

From Grosmont walk up the road for ¼ km and take the right fork, uphill for a further 1½ km.

Loc. **M27**, NZ 845 051, a viewpoint at the gate where the road reaches open moorland. On the northeast skyline there are quarries for building-stone in the Middle Jurassic sandstones. To the southwest the crest of the ridge is decorated with the waste rock from abandoned quarries and mines in the Cleveland Dyke. To the west is the long valley of the River Esk, which cuts through the Eskdale Dome (Journal **13**) in the valley due north from this Location.

The next Location is 6 km ahead. Stay on the road for 1 km, then take the footpath across Sleights Moor to the left. Turn right on the A169 for 100 metres, then left on a footpath, lane, and minor road to Littlebeck. After crossing the bridge in the village take the footpath to Falling Foss. For the first ½ km the path leads through rough ground left by quarrying for alum. It is now so covered by woodland that it's hard to picture it as a former industrial site. The steps at NZ 882 048 climb an exposure of Lower Jurassic mudstone.

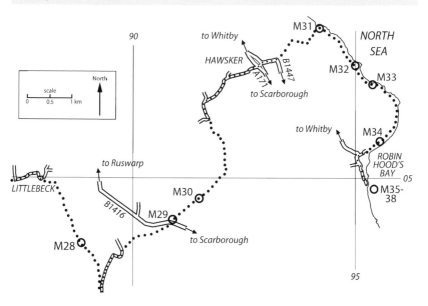

Littlebeck to Robin Hood's Bay.

249

Continue on the path, rising steeply through the Middle Jurassic sandstones. At the highest point, The Hermitage is a shelter carved out of a single bed of channel sandstone 4 metres thick (the river that deposited it must have been both deep and wide).

After 100 metres take the fork to the right, and ½ km further on fork to the right again (signposted to Falling Foss). The next Location is in 100 metres.

Loc. **M28**, NZ 888 036, a low cliff beside the path.

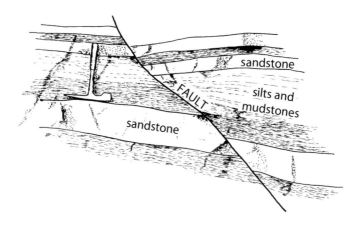

*Fig. **M28**. Thin sandstones alternating with mudstones and silts. The rocks are cut by several small faults, one of which is shown in the drawing. Remarkably, they are the only faults, of any size, we have seen in the Moors.*

These thinly bedded fine-grained sediments are floodplain deposits. Together with the thick channel sandstones and the coal we have seen earlier they make up the coastal-plain environment of the Middle Jurassic.

Walk on to Midge Hall and Falling Foss, where May Beck tumbles scenically over a hard sandstone at the base of the Middle Jurassic.

*Falling Foss in flood. A shingle bank of rock
fragments has collected in the plunge pool.*

From here downstream May Beck has eroded a narrow gorge in the soft Lower Jurassic mudstones within the much wider valley defined by the more resistant Middle Jurassic sandstones. The gorge has formed since the end of the Ice Age.

Between Falling Foss and Sneaton Low Moor (NZ 900 036), 3 km ahead, the Walk rises almost to the top of the Middle Jurassic, but the bedrock is out of sight below a cover of boulder clay and vegetation.

It is 3 km to the next Location. From Falling Foss walk on along the path through the wood until you reach the road at NZ 892 024. There turn sharply left and stay on the road to New May Beck Farm. A footpath leads across the moor to the right (northeast). Stop briefly at the B1416 road.

Loc. **M29**, NZ 907 040, where the Route crosses the road.

At this point you are 1½ km southeast of a new mine working potash deposits in Permian rocks 1500 metres below your feet. Journal **15** gives a short explanation.

Walk on along the footpath northeastwards from the road. Stop for a moment anywhere in the next kilometre with a clear view down the broad valley towards Whitby.

Loc. **M30**, on the path, near NZ 917 047.

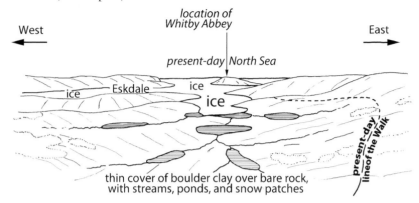

*Fig. **M30**. A cartoon of the view towards Whitby as it might have been near the end of the Ice Age.*

Using the drawing as a guide, imagine the scenery with ice covering the North Sea and extending up the Esk valley, the land surface very different from that of today, and an icy wind blowing.

> *The lack of bedrock exposures, because of the cover of boulder clay, continues all the way to the coast. Long views to Whitby and its Abbey, and the prospect of the magnificent coastal exposures, offer some compensation. The next Location is 6 km ahead.*
>
> *At NZ 920 059 the path joins an overgrown track to a tarmac road, where you go straight on. After ½ km, at a junction in a dip of the road, turn right towards Hawsker. At the crossroads with the A171 go straight on and in the centre of the village turn right on the B1447. In 300 metres the road turns right (temptingly to Robin Hood's Bay), but go straight ahead along a tarmac road through a caravan site. A footpath leads downhill to the coast and the next Location.*

THE DINOSAUR COAST

Loc. **M31**, NZ 942 083, the cliff-edge at Maw Wyke Hole.

This is the first view of the Yorkshire Dinosaur Coast (though dinosaur fossils – bones or footprints – are hard to find; the best ones are in museums).

West East

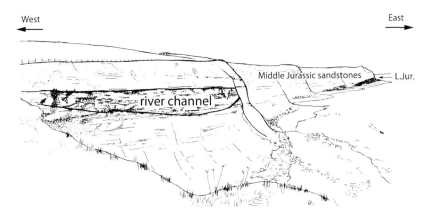

*Fig. **M31**. The view northeast at Maw Wyke Hole, showing part of the Middle Jurassic, with a prominent channel in the near cliff.*

The channel was eroded when a river was in flood, cutting into the parallel layering of the sandstones below. When the strength of the flow decreased the channel filled with sand. This is a further instalment of the picture of a wide coastal plain in the Middle Jurassic which we have been building all the way from Beacon Hill.

A thin coal seam at the base of the cliffs was visited by William Smith (1769-1839) – he is known as the "Father of English Geology" for his brilliant understanding of the significance of strata and the use of fossils for dating and correlating rocks.

Walk on for 1½ km to the top of the high cliff at Normanby Stye Batts. The long low hills inland from the path are drumlins.

Loc. **M32**, NZ 950 074, Normanby Stye Batts. On a clear day Flamborough Head can be seen 48 km south along the coast (above the white coastguard lookout point in the middle distance). The rocks there are in the Chalk, at the top of the Cretaceous, 1000 metres higher in the stratigraphic sequence, and 90 million years younger, than the Middle Jurassic rocks. It's a reasonable assumption that the rocks you are standing on here were buried by at least that thickness of younger sediments.

Walk on for ½ km to a lower point on the cliff.

Loc. **M33**, NZ 954 070. Clock Case Nab gives an extensive view of the rocks in the cliff at Normanby Stye Batts.

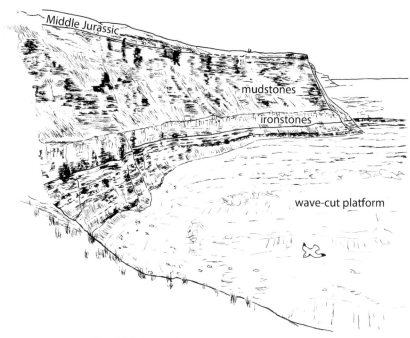

*Fig. **M33**. Most of the cliff is Lower Jurassic, with the base of the Middle Jurassic at the top.*

The thickness of the mudstones and their lateral extent (we have been walking across them all the way from Beacon Hill) give some idea of the quantity of rock being eroded at the time. Most of it came from the area of the original Pennine mountains and Southern Uplands of Scotland.

The impressive wave-cut platform is 200 metres wide at low tide.

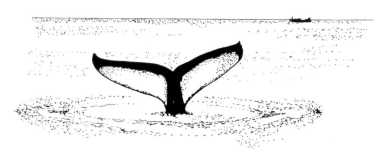

Whales can sometimes be seen from the cliff-top.

Continue round the coast for 2 km. Robin Hood's Bay, first the coastal feature and later the town, come into view.

THE ROBIN HOOD'S BAY HALF-DOME

Loc. **M34**, NZ 956 058, a seat on the cliff-edge by the kissing gate at the edge of Rocket Post Field. This gives a welcome prospect of the end of the Walk in Robin Hood's Bay.

Geologically, and especially if the tide is low, there is a superb view of the wave-cut platform and the semicircular outcrop pattern of the Lower Jurassic rocks. The dips all the way round the bay are landwards, at 5° or less, away from a point below the sea half-way between here and Ravenscar. More resistant sandstones of the Middle Jurassic form the half-ring of hills surrounding the bay, again dipping away from the centre of the bay. The dips of the layers define the three-dimensional shape of the Robin Hood's Bay half-dome.

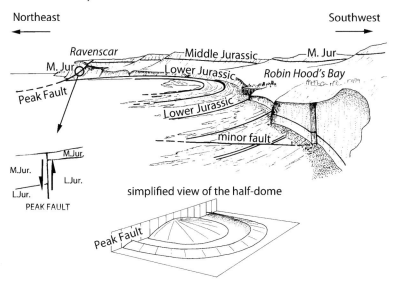

*Fig. **M34**. Panoramic view of Robin Hood's Bay at low tide, looking SSE from Rocket Post Field (the drawing is exaggerated vertically).*

The left inset shows the Peak Fault as it would appear viewed from the sea. The fault has moved the Jurassic rocks down on the east side by about 130 metres and it also makes the eastern side of the half-dome. The lower drawing is a simple geometrical model of the half-dome.

In the right foreground a small fault cuts the Lower Jurassic rocks on the foreshore and in the cliff. It is not related to the much larger Peak Fault.

For more ideas about the half-dome see Journal **15**.

There is just 1½ km to the end of the Walk at the slipway in Robin Hood's Bay.

This is the moment for us to congratulate you on your achievement. We hope that the 300 km of the Walk has been rewarding, not least through what the rocks and scenery have revealed about 500 million years of Earth history.

The coastal exposures at Robin Hood's Bay are among the finest in the country. If you have time and energy it's worth spending some of it looking at the rocks here. Among other attractions, you can neatly complete your knowledge of the geology of northern England by looking at the oldest and the youngest rocks in the story.

THE BEACH AT ROBIN HOOD'S BAY

First, some very necessary words of warning:

The tide comes up to the base of the cliffs, and it is dangerously easy to get cut off. The rocks are often covered with seaweed, and can be very slippery. Cliff falls are frequent, some very large. For your own safety, don't go close to the cliffs, and keep one eye on the tide, and the other eye on your feet.

The beach at Robin Hood's Bay at low tide.

COASTAL EROSION

Boulder clay covers the upper parts of the cliffs. It is much more easily eroded than the Jurassic mudstones, and frequently slumps down the cliffs. The concrete wall below the houses protects the village from sea erosion which in the past has claimed many houses and lives. Below the cliffs each side of the village huge blocks of **gneiss** provide rock-armouring to diminish the effects of erosion.

GNEISS – THE OLDEST ROCKS IN THE STORY

Loc. **M35**, NZ 952 047, the sea defences at the south end of the concrete promenade (if the tide is high these can be reached from the steps that go up beside the old coastguard station). The blocks of gneiss are from a megaquarry in Norway, some 600 km northeast along the same Caledonian mountain belt that built the Lake District.

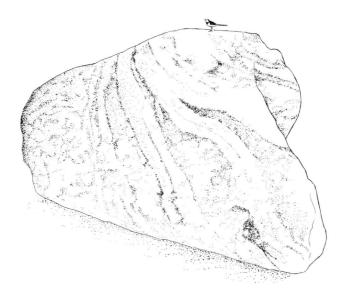

*Fig. **M35**. Gneiss boulder. Bands of white granitic composition alternate with highly metamorphosed rock of originally muddy composition.*

The rock was formed in the core of the mountain belt (perhaps 20-30 km below the surface). At this depth in the Earth's crust temperatures are high enough to melt granite, and most rock types are in a ductile state and easily deformed by the powerful forces of the continental collision. The folding of the compositional banding shows the extreme deformation the rocks have suffered.

Rocks such as these form the lowest parts of the crust in every continent and include some of the oldest dated rocks in the world – going back to about 3800 million years.

Walk south along the shore, looking for a clean exposure of brown boulder clay overlying grey Jurassic mudstone at the base of the cliff.

BOULDER CLAY – THE YOUNGEST ROCKS IN THE STORY

Loc. **M36**, between NZ 953 047 and 953 043. Locations vary, depending on falls and slumps of the boulder clay.

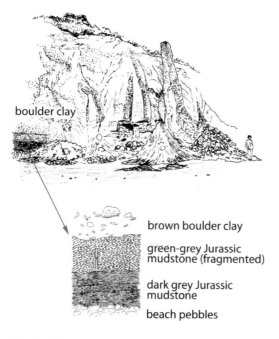

boulder clay

brown boulder clay

green-grey Jurassic mudstone (fragmented)

dark grey Jurassic mudstone

beach pebbles

Fig. M36. The unstable cliffs ½ km south of the slipway at Robin Hood's Bay. Inset: detail of the exposure of Jurassic bedrock at the base of the cliff.

The boulder clay is a product of melting debris-laden ice about 10,000 years ago. One can only guess at the amount of rock material carried in the ice (10%?, 50%?), but clearly the glacier was much thicker than the present height of the cliffs.

The dark-grey Jurassic mudstone below the boulder clay is 190 million years old. The overlying green-grey mudstone is the same rock broken into small fragments still more or less in place. It was deformed by the weight of the glacier sliding over it, and lubricated the movement of the ice.

ERRATIC PEBBLES AND BOULDERS ON THE SHORE

Browsing the shore can be instructive as well as entertaining. Most of the pebbles on the beach are local Jurassic rocks, but some are **erratics** carried here by glaciers. Some you may recognise from earlier days of your walk – for instance, Carboniferous limestones with shells or corals, and dolerite from the Cleveland Dyke. Boulders of Shap Granite up to half-a-metre across are fairly common and easily recognised.

Loc. **M37**, NZ 955 042. The bank of shingle ½ km south of the slipway usually offers a good variety of pebbles.

Erratics can be used to map the routes of the various glaciers that at different times in the Ice Age have moved over the area.

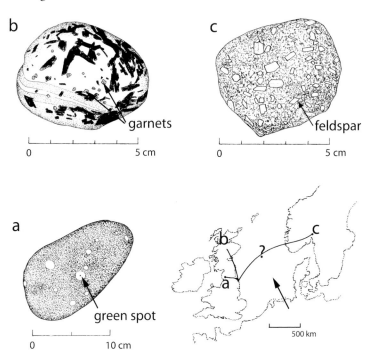

Fig. M37. Three particularly distinctive pebbles and their probable origins.

a   *Red sandstone with circular (spherical) green spots, from the Permo-Triassic. The labelled green spot has a speck of black plant material at its centre.*

b   *"Calc-silicate", a metamorphosed muddy limestone from the Scottish Highlands, white with small red garnets and large black crystals (a mineral called hornblende).*

c   *"Rhomb porphyry", a volcanic rock, similar to those in the Oslo area of Norway, sandy-yellow or medium-grey with white feldspar crystals.*

Map: Northwest Europe, showing origins of the three pebbles.

JURASSIC ROCKS AT ROBIN HOOD'S BAY

The Jurassic bedrock of the foreshore is mudstone with harder layers of siltstone or muddy limestone making the scars or reefs. The cliffs on the north and south sides of the bay are sandstone overlying the mudstone.

Loc. **M38**, anywhere in the bay, including Loc. **M37**.

Keeping safety in mind, you can see a wide variety of marine sediments at different locations. Pebbles and boulders offer a safe way of looking at the rocks, so no specific Locations are suggested here. Robin Hood's Bay has a great reputation as an area for finding fossils, though a brief search can be either very disappointing or very rewarding.

MUDSTONES

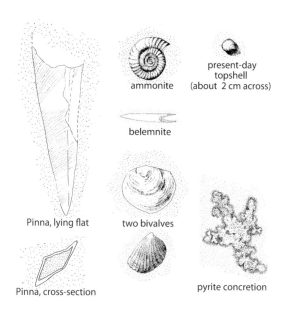

ammonite

present-day topshell
(about 2 cm across)

belemnite

Pinna, lying flat

two bivalves

Pinna, cross-section

pyrite concretion

Fig. M38/1. Some of the fossils that can be found in the mudstones at Robin Hood's Bay. The modern topshell provides the scale.

One of the *Pinna* (**bivalve**) fossils lies flat on the bedding plane of the mudstone, the other shows the lozenge-shaped cross-section corresponding to its life-position on the sea floor. The irregular-shaped cluster of dull-yellow pyrite (iron sulphide) crystals was formed as a concretion from chemical solutions after the sediment was buried.

The mudstones were formed in a moderately deep marine environment, but land was near enough for occasional storms to bring in the layers of coarser sediments.

CONCRETIONS

Some of the harder layers and scars within the mudstones are bands of rounded or elongated concretions, usually smooth and dark red-brown in colour. When they are broken open they reveal a very distinctive pattern of white veins.

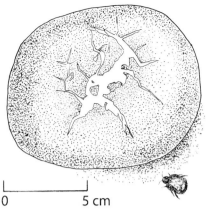

Fig. M38/2. An iron-rich concretion from a mudstone, broken across the centre. The colour changes from red-brown at the centre to dark grey at the outside. The white veins are calcite.

Sorry to disappoint, but this is not a dinosaur egg (even though the calcite veins do look like some mythical beast).

SILTSTONES AND SANDSTONES

There is a great variety of siltstone and sandstone pebbles. These come from the higher layers of the cliffs, and are usually pale grey or yellow-grey. Just two are illustrated here.

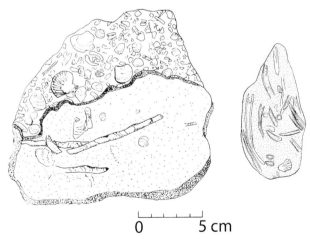

Fig. M38/3. Parts of two sandy pebbles. On the left is a layer crowded with broken mollusc shells and an overlying layer with fossil burrows of a marine animal and some broken shells. On the right is a siltstone with curved tubular tusk shells.

The rich and varied fossil assemblages of the siltstones and sandstones show that there were many different situations within a shallow near-shore marine environment. This part of the Jurassic sea was warmer than, but otherwise like, near-shore areas of Robin Hood's Bay. (You may remember our comment at St Bees that the beach scene there can be used as a key to understanding processes in the past.)

ROUNDING OFF...

And there is another throwback to the beginning of the Walk – almost making it seem like a round tour! Triassic rocks are just below the Jurassic at the centre of the Robin Hood's Bay half-dome. Another 150 metres of erosion would expose the same kind of red desert sandstones that made the cliffs at St Bees Head.

JOURNAL 15 – ROBIN HOOD'S BAY

Houses in Robin Hood's Bay.

MINERAL RESOURCES OF THE MOORS

The economic value of many of the rocks (building stone, brick clays, ironstone, alum, coal, jet, roadstone), much of it on a relatively small scale, brought local prosperity at various times to the Moors. As those industries declined, farming, and more recently tourism based on the scenic value of the landscape, continued. At the present day there are prospects for development of potash and gas, though these are controversial because of their location within the North York Moors National Park.

AN ANCIENT SEA WITH MODERN VALUE (Loc. M29).

The existence of saline deposits in northwest Europe has been known for many years. The rocks were formed when Britain was in latitude 10-20° north of the equator. The climate was hot and dry, similar to the Sahara desert or the inland basins of central Asia. The scenery of the Permian included a partly enclosed sea (given the name Zechstein Sea). Its western margin was only a few kilometres inland from the present North Yorkshire coast. Evaporation of the sea created a sequence of layers of soluble salts. They are mined at Boulby, on the coast 25 km northwest of Robin Hood's Bay.

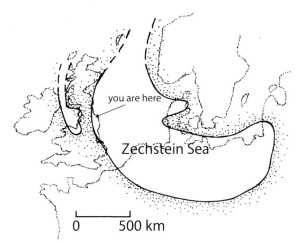

The Zechstein Sea in northern Europe 260 million years ago. A smaller sea lay on the west side of the Pennines; evaporation there produced the buried salt deposits of the Vale of Eden and Cheshire. The surrounding land areas were covered by desert.

Recently, exploratory deep drill-holes have provided more detail on the extent and composition of the deposits. Layers rich in potash (of particular value as a fertiliser) occur 1500 metres below ground near Robin Hood's Bay; a mine is currently being developed to extract it.

These deeply buried rocks occur only a few hundred metres below the level of the Triassic sandstones which you saw at the very beginning of the Walk at St Bees Head (Loc. **C6**).

CONCRETIONS (Loc. M38).

Many kinds of sedimentary rock contain rounded or elongated hard compact masses called concretions. They may be any size from a few centimetres to a metre in length or diameter. Their relative resistance to erosion means that they often stand out from the surrounding sediment. Sometimes they are isolated and seemingly random in distribution, or they may form nearly continuous layers.

Concretions are formed early in the process of consolidating a soft sediment into a rock. They commonly consist of calcium carbonate (calcite), silica (quartz), or iron minerals. They are entirely inorganic in origin, though the process may start with a fossil as a nucleus. Clearly the process of turning soft mud into mudstone is chemically more complex than appears at first sight.

THE JURASSIC ROCKS OF THE NORTH YORK MOORS

In the final 80 km we have walked over rocks of the Lower and Middle Jurassic, deposited in the area known as the Cleveland Basin – a gulf of the early North Sea.

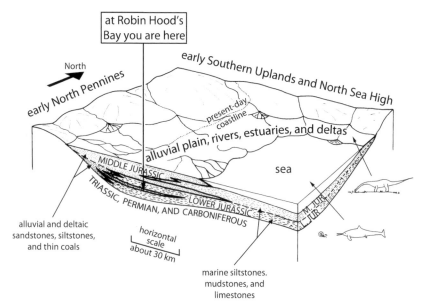

An impression of northern England and part of the Cleveland Basin as they might have been during the Middle Jurassic.

The vertical cross-section at the front of the drawing shows the older rocks of the Jurassic. The heavy line migrating up through the section shows how the position of the coastline, separating the areas of deposition of land and sea sediments, changed over 40 million years or so. The location of the coastline and the depth of the sea determined the kind of sediment that was deposited.

THE ROBIN HOOD'S BAY HALF-DOME – A PROBLEMATIC STRUCTURE (Loc. *M34*).

At low tide you can see nearly all of the half-dome of Jurassic rocks. It is the easternmost on-land appearance of the Cleveland Anticline (Journal **13**). The Jurassic rocks are cut across and displaced by the Peak Fault, which brings Middle Jurassic rocks down to sea level at Ravenscar.

In spite of its simple appearance, the half-dome may have a more complicated history. The date of the folding can be formally determined from the local evidence only as later than the youngest rocks that are affected – Middle Jurassic. Evidence from a wider area shows that there were episodes of folding during the Jurassic, and also as a distant effect of the formation of the Alps 65 million years ago and 1000 km to the southeast. How much each of these events affected the rocks at Robin Hood's Bay is difficult to determine.

The Peak Fault adds a further puzzle – there is no matching eastern half of the Robin Hood's Bay half-dome below the sea, and it is not clear what takes its place. However, though the Cleveland Anticline appears to stop at the coast, the rocks continue:

THE NORTH YORK MOORS AND THE NORTH SEA

If we could use remote sensing to look beneath the waves of the North Sea we would see that the same kind of rocks and structures continue eastwards for many tens of kilometres.

The two rock-types we have seen most often in the Moors – mudstone and sandstone – and their nearly horizontal layering may have made the geology seem rather simple. But in fact these are some of the features that have made the North Sea a significant part of Britain's past and present prosperity. Mudstones are potential source rocks for oil, permeable sandstones are potential reservoir rocks, and gently dipping arch-shaped folds are potential structures for holding reserves of oil and gas. Seismic surveying is used to locate likely prospects for drilling.

POST-GLACIAL SCENERY OF THE NORTH YORK MOORS AND COAST

The most obvious effects of the Ice Age on the inland scenery come from its latest stages – features like the meltwater channels and the landslides. The general shape of the Moors as an upland area relative to the North Sea was established long before the glaciation. During the Ice Age sea level was about 100 metres lower than it is now, so the present wide wave-cut platform at the base of the cliffs was probably created in the last 10,000 years. Erosion continues, and can be heard as a nearly continuous tinkle of falling pieces of mudstone, with periodic larger cliff falls. Where the cliffs are made of boulder clay erosion is even more rapid (Loc. **M36**). Further south, the coast of East Yorkshire is retreating at dangerously fast rates, up to several metres per year.

GEOLOGICAL HAZARDS

In the course of the Walk we have seen many examples that show the power of Earth processes – explosive volcanic activity, big faults and their associated earthquakes, climatic changes and variations of sea level, the Great Dying, rivers in flood, landslides, cliff falls. We said earlier that present-day Earth processes can be used to understand how rocks were formed in the past. The argument goes equally the other way round – the evidence of rock-forming processes in the past can be used to understand present-day risks. Recognising environments which are potentially hazardous is the first step to taking action to minimise their risks. This is just one of the many ways in which the study of rocks and scenery is valuable to society.

GEODIVERSITY

Another outcome of the Walk has been to show the remarkable diversity of rocks and scenery. Our traverse across northern England gave us just a small sample of the great variety of rocks and environments to be found on or near the Earth's surface. Many more can be found elsewhere and still more have existed in the past.

We have seen that rocks can be made on land or in the sea, in volcanoes or in glaciers, in continental collisions or in new oceans. Looking at fine detail gives more precise interpretations, such as the source of sedimentary material and how it was deposited, the different kinds of volcanic eruption, or the conditions that created and preserved the scenery of ancient land surfaces. Rocks can be studied using the minerals that compose them, the fossils they contain, and the structures that show how they were formed and deformed. Relations between rock units reveal their time-sequence, so that we can work out the history of an area like northern England and the evolution of successive environments within it.

Likewise, scenery can be understood at every scale from the size and shape of continents, mountain chains, and river systems, down to details of the shape of individual exposures of rock. Different types of scenery are formed by processes of erosion or of deposition, and in environments as varied as deserts and glaciers. And that's just the scenery we can see on land – below the surface of the sea, sediments are being deposited right now and will solidify into sequences of rock layers. The continued effect of powerful Earth movements will be to raise some of these layers above sea level to become the rocks and scenery of the future.

In human terms, the rocks underlying the scenery determine whether we make our living by farming, industry, or by tourism, and whether we live over buried natural resources such as coal, oil, or potash. And by building towns and cities, dams and quarries, roads and airports humans have had an increasing influence in shaping the landscape. Making use of Earth resources changes their distribution on the surface, and in the case of fossil fuels extends that effect into the Earth's atmosphere.

The ways to study rocks are nearly as diverse as the rocks themselves. They are based on the established methods of physics, chemistry, and biology, and on newer subjects like climate change and planetary evolution. The methods are adapted to the distinctive feature of geology – that most rocks and scenery were formed millions or thousands of years ago – hence the relevance of the detective analogy that we proposed earlier.

Understanding rocks and scenery is essentially about understanding the processes that created them. Although the study of geology can get quite technical, all that is needed for the everyday enjoyment of rocks and scenery is a discerning eye and an inquiring mind. We hope we have persuaded you that geology is a fascinating, diverse, and accessible subject that can enhance your experience of the landscape wherever you walk.

7. HISTORICAL SYNTHESIS AND PLATE TECTONICS

You have now completed your Walk and can celebrate your achievement, remembering the 300 kilometres you have travelled, the people you have met, the sights you have seen, your thoughts and feelings on the journey. Enrich your experience of the rocks and scenery too by reflecting on your journey in geological space and time. The line of the Walk traverses most of the last 500 million years of the history of northern England – an inspired choice by Alfred Wainwright. We round off the Walk with a brief history of northern England set in the global model of plate tectonics.

We have travelled forwards (and sometimes backwards) in time across rocks formed in a great diversity of environments – from calm seas to continental collisions, from vigorous erosion to the formation of huge thicknesses of sediment, from rock-melting temperatures to glacial freezing. We have seen the evidence for ancient land-surfaces represented by unconformities, and inferred the major upheavals of the Earth's crust that produced them.

To adapt a well-known quotation – we have seen plenty of rocks, but not necessarily in the right order. The key to understanding what happened, and to some extent why it happened, is to look at northern England in a global context. Using the reconstructions of plate tectonics we can map the successive changes in our geographical, structural, and climatic positions on the surface of the Earth. At least five major changes in the configurations of plates had an effect on the history of northern England:

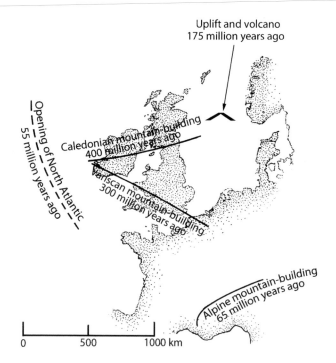

Northwest Europe and some plate boundaries.

Rocks older than 500 million years: the deepest basement

The oldest rocks we have seen on the Walk must obviously have been deposited on still older rocks which are not exposed in northern England. We can infer, by analogy with other parts of the Caledonian mountain chain in Scotland and elsewhere, that the older and deeper rocks were metamorphosed sediments and igneous rocks like the Norwegian gneisses seen in the coastal defences at Robin Hood's Bay.

The Early Palaeozoic, 500-450 million years ago: oceans and volcanoes

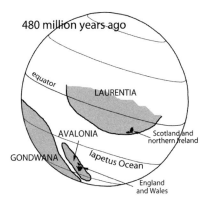

480 million years ago

The world view to have in mind is that 500 million years ago there were two large continents – Gondwana (now Africa and the rest of the southern continents) near the south pole, and Laurentia (present-day North America and Greenland – and also Scotland and the north of Ireland) in the north. A broad ocean, named Iapetus, lay between them. Around 500 million years ago a small piece of the Gondwana continent, given the name Avalonia, broke away and moved northwards across the Iapetus Ocean. The area that is now northern England was near the north coast of Avalonia.

The oldest rocks that we saw in situ, the Ordovician mudstones, were deposited in deep sea on the north side of Avalonia. A present-day geographical analogue is the Atlantic Ocean adjacent to South America.

For a short time 450 million years ago the northward drift of Avalonia was effected by subduction (destruction) of the Iapetus oceanic plate southwards below Avalonia.

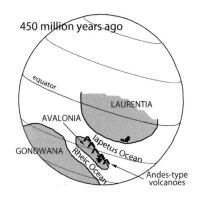

450 million years ago

Magma that was produced as a consequence of the subduction created the Ordovician volcanic rocks of the central Lake District. The Ennerdale Granite is a deeper-level part of the volcanic system. The Andes mountains on the Pacific side of South America are currently forming in the same plate-tectonic situation.

450-420 million years ago: a narrowing ocean

The Iapetus Ocean continued to get narrower and shallower during the later part of the Early Palaeozoic. Rocks of this age are not seen on the line of the Walk, but are exposed in the south of the Lake District.

Continental collision, 425-390 million years ago: the Caledonian mountain-building

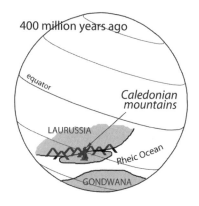

The inevitable collision of Avalonia with the larger Laurentia continent created the Caledonian mountain chain – a situation analogous to the geologically more recent collision of India with Asia. The Iapetus Suture joining the two continents crosses northern England on a WSW-ENE line from the Solway Firth to the northeast coast near Berwick. The enlarged continent is given the name Laurussia.

The area of northern England formed foothills to the south of the main mountain belt in Scotland. The collision caused deformation of the Lake District rocks, with crustal thickening and uplift, metamorphism, and the production of granites by melting of the thickened crust. England, Wales, Scotland, and Ireland were united within the new amalgamated continent and from now on behaved geologically as a single tectonic unit, forming the basement for all the younger rocks.

The Pennine Fault was probably initiated about now. It continued to be active for millions of years.

The Caledonian Unconformity: the Devonian, 420-360 million years ago, and a desert landscape

Britain was now in an arid tropical latitude south of the equator. The Caledonian mountains were exposed to erosion, which continued for much of the next 50 million years – approximately the time-span of the Devonian system. The erosion products were carried south into the Old Red Sandstone desert of the Midlands and South Wales – equivalent to the alluvial plains of the Indus and Ganges rivers at the present day.

The Carboniferous, 360-300 million years ago: clear seas and deltas

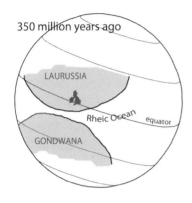

During the Carboniferous, northern England was close to the equator. The land surface on which the earliest Carboniferous sediments were deposited had been reduced to low topography and was slowly subsiding into warm, clear, shallow seas within the Laurussian continent. Some parts of northern England, known as blocks, remained as islands for longer than adjacent troughs (the latter now form the Vale of Eden and lower Teesdale). Eventually the whole of northern England was submerged, and deltas advanced from rivers eroding the Caledonian mountains in the north. Deposition of limestones, mudstones, and sandstones as repeated ("Yoredale") cycles was caused by changes of sea level influenced by glaciations of polar regions. The Mississippi delta is a present-day analogue.

An important igneous event at the end of the Carboniferous was the intrusion of a huge amount of dolerite magma to form the Whin Sill. It outcrops in the Pennine escarpment just north of the line of the Walk.

Another continental collision, 370-290 million years ago: the Variscan mountain-building

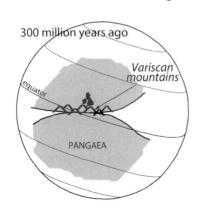

Other global changes had been going on during the Carboniferous. The Rheic Ocean between Gondwana and Laurussia had been closing. At the end of the Carboniferous the two large continents collided along a line through southwest England in another mountain-building episode – the Variscan – creating the supercontinent of Pangaea.

The effects of the mountain-building in northern England were folding and faulting. Erosion created the land surface (the Variscan unconformity) on which the Permian was deposited.

The Permian and Triassic, 300-200 million years ago: deserts and evaporating seas

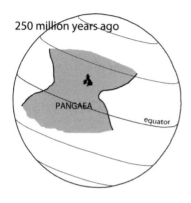

250 million years ago

PANGAEA

equator

Britain was now north of the equator, near the centre of Pangaea. The area was an arid desert of wind-blown sands and deposits of flash floods, like the present-day Sahara. For part of the time northern England formed a gulf of a shallow sea (the Zechstein Sea) covering part of the Pangaean continent. The Persian Gulf is a modern analogue. Evaporation of the sea water produced thick layers of commercially valuable soluble salts. The sandstones act as reservoir rocks for rich accumulations of oil and gas. The mineral ores of the Pennines were also formed at about this time.

Globally, the boundary between Permian and Triassic is marked by the extinction of 90% of all life-forms. In the desert that was then Britain, however, there was so little life that the event passed relatively unnoticed.

The Jurassic, 200-150 million years ago: another coastal environment

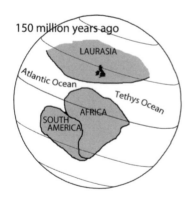

150 million years ago

LAURASIA

Atlantic Ocean

Tethys Ocean

AFRICA

SOUTH AMERICA

Pangaea began to split, creating the central Atlantic Ocean. Britain was on the northern continent, named Laurasia. A large volcano developed 175 million years ago in the central North Sea; associated uplift and erosion produced an unconformity between the Lower and Middle Jurassic in northern England.

Britain had continued to move north and was now in latitudes similar to the Mediterranean. Northern England was close to a shoreline between low-lying land and sea, making a variety of sedimentary environments on the general theme of rivers and deltas alternating with marine deposits.

An important group of marine fossils was the ammonites. Dinosaurs walked the land; their tracks are sometimes preserved, and more rarely their skeletons.

The Cretaceous and Tertiary, 145-2.6 million years ago: covering the older rocks

Sediments younger than the Jurassic (apart from the Quaternary) are not seen underfoot on the Walk, though the Cretaceous Chalk hills are visible to the south from high points on the Moors. Southwards along the east coast, Cretaceous and younger rocks extend into southeast England, and the same rocks are present in the North Sea Basin. They are mostly shallow-sea deposits, many of them richly fossiliferous. The same sediments, now removed by erosion, can be presumed to have covered most of the rocks we saw on the Walk.

And another collision of continents, 65 million years ago to the present day: the Alpine mountain-building

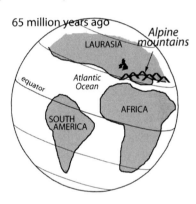

Northward drift of Africa (and India) towards Laurasia produced the Alps (and Himalayas).

In Britain the distant continental collision caused only gentle folding and tilting. Erosion exposed the sequence of rocks as we now see them along the line of the Walk, progressively younger from west to east – the Lower Palaeozoic of the Lake District, the Carboniferous of the Dales, the Permo-Triassic of the Vale of Mowbray, and the Jurassic of the Moors. On the east side of the Pennine watershed the erosion products of these rocks were carried eastwards into the developing North Sea Basin.

Continental splitting, 60 million years ago to the present day: the opening of the North Atlantic, and the Cleveland Dyke

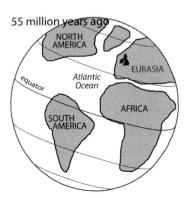

Splitting of the Laurasia continent extended the Atlantic Ocean to the north. The global pattern of the continents was now recognisably similar to that of the present day.

The Cleveland Dyke was one of many dykes related to the development of the Mid-Atlantic Ridge.

The Quaternary, 2.6 million years ago to the present day: the Ice Age

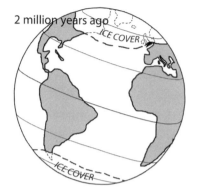

2 million years ago

ICE COVER

ICE COVER

Global cooling led to the formation of ice-caps and glaciers in northern Britain. Being so recent geologically, there is abundant evidence of its effects in the rocks and the scenery. Erosion produced numerous features, grandest of which are the **U**-shaped valleys of the Lake District. The glaciers transported huge quantities of eroded bedrock to deposit the boulder clay which covers much of the low ground, as in the Vale of Mowbray.

The final melting of the ice raised sea level globally by about 100 metres, and the English Channel became a seaway separating Britain from continental Europe. All rocks, including those of the Quaternary, are now exposed to erosion, which is particularly vigorous along the coasts.

The present, and maybe the future?

The Earth is a dynamic planet, continuously changing and evolving. Look at any scene in the natural environment and you can see changes in progress. Rivers carry the products of erosion of older rocks and deposit them as new sediments. Waves and tides alter the shape of the coastline. Volcanoes add new rocks to the surface of the earth. The slow but powerful movements of tectonic plates change the configuration of continents and oceans. It's not possible to predict exactly what our planet will look like a million years hence, but of one thing we can be sure – the processes that we have seen in the past (with the added influence of human activity) will continue into the future.

GLOSSARY

The brief explanations here relate specifically to usage in this book. To avoid too many technical terms we have over-simplified the meanings of some words which are more exactly defined elsewhere. The references are to Location numbers and the Journals.

alluvial fan sediments deposited in the form of a low-angle cone, resulting from a change of gradient of a stream from steep to gentle (**L7**).

alluvium sediments deposited by a stream or river (Journal **1**).

ammonites diverse extinct group of molluscs having a chambered shell coiled in a plane spiral (Journal **11**).

anticline arch-shaped fold (**M15**, Journal **13**).

arête knife-edged ridge between two glacial valleys or **corries** (**L65**).

ash fall product of an explosive volcanic eruption, resulting in airborne **magma** droplets, depositing a **bedded tuff** (Journal **2**).

ash flow product of an explosive volcanic eruption, resulting in a flowing cloud of gas and **magma** droplets, depositing a **welded tuff** (Journal **2**).

basement continental crust which has become relatively rigid and onto which younger rocks have been deposited (Journal **5**).

bed layer of sediment or of **tuff**, deposited in a single episode (Journal **1**, **C2**).

bedded tuff layered rock erupted by a volcano and composed mostly of ash particles (Journal **2**, **L15**).

bedding plane the surface separating one **bed** from the next (Journal 1, **C2**).

bedrock rocks ranging in age from the very oldest to the beginning of the Ice Age (Journal **1**). Contrasted with **superficial rocks**.

belemnites extinct group of molluscs related to the **ammonites**. The fossils are pointed cylinders of **calcite** (Journal **11**).

bivalve group of molluscs with two shells (Journal **10**).

body fossil fossilised remains of the body of an animal or plant. See **trace fossil.**

boulder clay sediment deposited directly from melting ice and composed of a wide range of particle sizes from clay to boulders (Journal **1**, **L36**, **M36**).

brachiopods group of marine animals with two shells (Journal **5**).

breccia rock composed of broken fragments of other rocks (Journal **2**, **L12**).

calcite mineral – calcium carbonate.

caldera a roughly circular structure, several kilometres across, resulting from collapse of part of a volcano (Journal **4**).

chert hard flinty sedimentary rock made of very fine-grained silica (**D39**).

cleavage preferred direction of splitting of a rock due to the growth of small flaky crystals in parallel orientation during compression (Journal **2**, **L22**).

coal rock derived from plant material (e.g. peat), now more or less pure carbon (**C6**, Journal **13**).

coarse-grained rock (or part of a rock) made of large crystals or grains (Journal **2**).

constructive plate boundary the boundary between two **plates** where new **oceanic crust** is created (e.g. Mid-Atlantic Ridge) (Journal **14**).

continental collision the collision of two **plates** carrying **continental crust**, and resulting in **mountain-building** (Journals **4**, **5**).

continental crust the part of a **plate**, usually about 30 km thick, which makes the continents. Note that the area of continental crust includes shallow seas surrounding the land-mass (see next item).

continental shelf edge the boundary on a **plate** between **continental crust** and **oceanic crust** (Journal **14**). It is marked by an increase in depth from shallow sea to deep ocean.

coral group of colonial (reef-building) or solitary marine animals (Journal **5**).

corrie a high-level, roughly semicircular, steep-sided valley carved by a small glacier (**L48**).

crag-and-ledge feature on a hill-slope resulting from a sequence of alternating hard and soft layers in the bedrock (**L19**).

cross-bedding layers within a **bed** deposited at an angle to the original horizontal (**C2**).

crust the outermost solid layer of the Earth. See **continental crust**, **oceanic crust**.

cycle repeated sequence of sediments made by a cyclic process (Journal **7**).

delta wide flat area formed where a river joins a lake or the sea and divides into a pattern of **distributary** channels (**L11**, Journal **7**).

dip the angle of slope of a tilted **bed**, and its direction of tilt (**C4**).

dip slope hill-slope formed by the top surface of a tilted **bed** (**R7**).

displacement the amount of movement on a **fault** plane (Journal **4**).

distributary river channel formed as a stream or river divides in the downstream direction (Journal **7**).

dolerite dark-coloured **igneous** rock, making a large part of the **oceanic crust**, and forming **dykes** and other kinds of intrusion in **continental crust** (**L68**, **M25**).

drumlin long low rounded hill made of boulder clay (**R12**).

ductile style of deformation without fracturing, typically producing a **fold**. Contrasted with brittle deformation.

dyke long narrow, usually vertical or steeply inclined, intrusion of **igneous** rock (Journal **2**, **L9**, **M25**).

erratic boulder transported by ice, and not derived directly from the local bedrock (**C5**).

eruption the release of **magma** and gas from a volcano to make **lava**, **tuff**, and other volcanic products (Journal **2**).

exposure bedrock visible at the surface, not covered by **superficial rocks** or by soil or vegetation. Contrasted with **outcrop**.

fault structure made by brittle fracture of rocks, followed by displacement (**L33**, Journals **4**, **6**).

feldspar group of pale-coloured minerals (sodium, calcium, or potassium aluminium silicates) that make major amounts of nearly all kinds of **igneous** rocks (**D1**).

fine-grained rock (or part of a rock) made of small crystals or grains (Journal **2**).

floodplain essentially flat part of a river system, where sediments are deposited by periodic floods from the main river channel.

flow-banding structure in a **lava** resulting from flow before consolidation (**L20**).

fold structure resulting from **ductile** deformation of rocks (Journals **2**, **4**).

gangue parts of a mineral **vein** which have no economic value (**D34**).

gneiss rock from deep in the **continental crust**, typically banded and folded (**M35**).

goniatites ancestors of the **ammonites**, mainly Upper Palaeozoic in age (Journal **5**).

graded bed single **bed** in which the grain size changes gradationally from coarser to finer (**L3**).

granite coarse-grained **igneous** rock, largely **quartz** and **feldspar**, crystallised from a **magma** below the surface of the Earth (Journal **2**, **L10**, **D1**).

hot spot an area of continued volcanism not directly related to the structure of the underlying **plates** (Journal **4**).

igneous rock solidified from **magma** (Journal **2**). See **lava**, **tuff**, **granite**, **dolerite**.

intrusion **magma** emplaced and solidified below the surface of the Earth (Journal **2**).

ironstone rock which can be used as iron **ore** (**M26**).

joint brittle fracture of a rock, but without other movement. Joints are usually the result of contraction, e.g. by release of pressure after deep burial or by cooling from a high temperature (Journal **1**).

landslide flow or fall of large amounts of rock down a slope (**D21**, **M16**).

lava volcanic rock formed by the solidification of a flow of **magma** (Journal **2**, **L17**).

limestone sedimentary rock, made of **calcite**, and formed of the shells of marine animals (Journal **5**, **D40**).

magma molten rock; solidifies to make **igneous** rock (Journal **2**).

mantle outer 2300 km of the Earth, surrounded by the **continental** and **oceanic crust**. Very slow fluid movement of the mantle drives movement of the overlying crustal **plates** (Journal **14**).

metamorphism the process of changing the minerals and structure of a rock because of heat (**thermal**, around an igneous intrusion) or heat, pressure, and deformation (regional, in **continental collisions**). (Journal **2**).

mica mineral – a silicate of potassium and aluminium (white mica – muscovite), or the same with magnesium and iron (black mica – biotite); both kinds form flat, easily split crystals (**D1**, **D13**).

mid-ocean ridge the boundary between two **oceanic plates** where new oceanic **crust** is being created (Journals **4**, **14**).

misfit stream too small to have eroded the valley it occupies (**L5**).

moraine rock debris deposited by a glacier (**L25**). See also **terminal moraine**.

mountain-building the result of collision of two continents, such as Africa and Europe to make the Alps, or of an **oceanic** and a **continental plate**, such as the Pacific plate and South America to make the Andes (Journal **5**).

mudstone fine-grained rock, solidified from a mud (Journal **2**).

oceanic crust the part of a **plate**, about 10 km thick, made at a **constructive plate boundary**. Usually covered by deep ocean.

ore a rock from which economically valuable material can be extracted (**L46**, **D34**).

outcrop bedrock not directly visible because of a cover of **superficial rocks**. Contrasted with **exposure**.

plate a large segment of the surface of the Earth, above the **mantle**, composed of either **continental crust** or **oceanic crust** or of both kinds.

quartz mineral – silicon dioxide, the main component of sandstones, and also in mineral veins (**L21**).

reworked tuff **tuff** which has been deposited from a volcanic eruption and then eroded and re-deposited (**L33**).

sandstone sediment made mostly of **quartz** grains (Journal **1**).

scarp slope hill-slope in the opposite direction to the **dip** of **beds** (**R7**).

sea lily group of marine animals, related to sea urchins but growing on a stalk of cylindrical (sometimes five-pointed star-shapes) **calcite** plates (Journal **5**).

sedimentary rocks rocks made by solidification of sediments deposited at the surface of the Earth (Journals **1**, **2**).

sill **intrusion** of **magma** as a sheet parallel with the bedding of surrounding rocks (Journal **2**, **L16**, **D2**).

slate rock, originally fine-grained **tuff** or **mudstone**, which has been compressed so as to develop **cleavage** (Journal **2**, **L22**).

strike the compass direction of bedding or cleavage planes on a horizontal surface (necessarily at right angles to the **dip** direction) (**L2**).

subduction zone the sub-surface zone marking the boundary between two moving **plates**, one of which is moving downwards below the other. At the surface there is intense **volcanic** activity (Journal **4**). Continued movement may lead to **continental collision**.

superficial rocks sediments formed during and since the Ice Age, forming extensive deposits covering the **bedrock** (Journal **1**). **Boulder clay** and **alluvium** are superficial rocks.

suture the outcrop (or its continuation below the surface) of the boundary between two continents following a **continental collision** (Journal **5**).

terminal moraine ridge of **moraine** deposited at the temporarily stationary front edge of a glacier (**L26, D45**).

thermal metamorphism the process of changing the minerals and structure of a rock because of heat from an igneous intrusion (Journal **2, L8**).

till plain broad area of low relief, formerly covered by ice, and now by **boulder clay** (**D55**, Journal **10**).

trace fossil trace left by an animal moving through or on sediment (Journal **5**). See **body fossil**.

tuff rock solidified from the products of explosive volcanism. See **bedded tuff, reworked tuff, welded tuff** (Journal **2**).

unconformity the land surface formed by erosion of an older (usually folded) group of rocks, and onto which a younger group of rocks was deposited (**L75**, Journals **5, 10**).

vein long narrow sheet-like structure containing economic minerals, often filling the line of a **fault** (**L46, D34**).

volcanic rock produced by a volcano, as a lava or by explosive action, or rocks intruded near the surface as part of a volcano's plumbing system (Journal **2**).

welded tuff rock produced by a volcanic **ash flow** and consisting mostly of blobs of solidified **magma**, often flattened (Journal **2, L18**).

Yoredale cycle repeated sequence of limestone, mudstone, sandstone, (and sometimes coal), forming a major part of the Carboniferous (Journal **7**).

Index

About the Authors

Barry Butler was a lecturer in geology at the University of Oxford and a tutor with the Open University. He lives in Robin Hood's Bay, at the end of Wainwright's Coast-to-Coast Walk. Before that he lived at Hurst, in Swaledale, also on the line of the Walk.

John Gunner has been teaching geology to adults in the north of England since 1990 – for Lancaster, Liverpool, Newcastle and the Open Universities. He spent four years doing geological research in Antarctica and taught for ten years at Brathay Field Studies Centre near Ambleside. He has a geology degree from Oxford, a PhD from Ohio State University and a Certificate in Higher Education Course Design and Teaching from the Open University. He has a strong belief in using field work to make geology come alive.